Contents

Introduction

The Mental Warm-up Activities provide a structured scheme of work for developing mental mathematics strategies. The daily activities have been written to practise key mental maths skills, and address these using a variety of techniques:

- practising pre-requisite skills (e.g. partitioning numbers: 8 is 7 and 1, 6 and 2, 5 and 3, 4 and 4)
- building on two or more of these skills to develop a new strategy (e.g. adding 17 + 8 by partitioning 8 into 3 and 5, and knowing that 17 + 3 = 20)
- practising and extending known strategies (e.g. 127 + 8 =)
- using known strategies as pre-requisites for a new set of strategies, (e.g. related to a different operation)
- developing a 'memory bank' of key facts (e.g. addition bonds to 10, doubles to 10)
- using key facts to develop further strategies (e.g. 6 + 6 = 12 so 6 + 7 = 13).

How to use this book

To allow the teacher flexibility, the book is broken down into two sections:

Unit specific activities

For each Number Unit there are two whole class activities. Some of these relate directly to skills or sub-skills for that Unit. Some activities practise more general skills, and these will develop in strands throughout the book (a skills chart mapping this development is included on pages vii to ix). Often the two activities provided will be enough to cover the work required for that Unit.

Activity bank

For number Units that last longer than two days, or for Shape, Data and Measures Units, the teacher can select supplementary activities from the bank provided at the back of the book. The Activity Bank includes a wide variety of activities that address key skills. The activities in the bank can be used at any time alongside any topic, and often you will wish to revisit them throughout the year.

Together, these two types of activity will provide enough activities for one warm-up each day.

The activities

The mental activities are of three types:

Open-ended

These are activities where there may be several ways of getting a 'right' answer. Often a key benefit of the activity will be the discussion which the children have with you and each other about which strategies they have used. This is a good opportunity to go through several different ways of doing something with the whole class, so that different methods or techniques are shared and discussed.

Closed

These activities have one correct answer and usually, one preferred strategy to use. So, for example, when adding 9 to a 2-digit number, the activity may practise the specific technique of adding 10 and taking 1 away.

Memorising

These activities are designed to help children memorise a particular set of number facts, e.g. doubles of numbers to 10, addition bonds. Eventually each child will have a set of memorised facts that they know by heart. Certain key activities appear several times during the book to help reinforce these skills.

Generic activities

Most of the activities use similar formats and structures from Unit to Unit, and children will become familiar with these. These 'generic' activities are described in more detail on pages iv to vi.

Also included in each unit are a word of the week, a number of the week or a shape of the week. These can be used to develop children's use of the language and vocabulary of number both spoken ('tell me something about this week's number') and written ('write three things about this week's shape').

The number of the week can be used to develop mental dexterity, consolidate concepts and skills studied in a given Number Unit, and to develop the use and understanding of the language of number. For each number some sample tasks and facts are given.

The shape of the week can be used to increase awareness of the properties of shape and space, and to encourage the use of the associated language.

The word of the week can be used to develop use and understanding of the vocabulary of mathematics, and to consolidate language associated with the Unit being studied. Sometimes the 'word of the week' relates to vocabulary in the relevant Unit, sometimes the word is included to rehearse vocabulary met in the past. Children should be encouraged to both hear the word being used in different contexts, and to use the word in responses and statements.

Working partners

At the beginning of the year (or each term), place the children in pairs as 'working partners'. The pairs do not necessarily have to be matched by ability – two children of different abilities can help each other. Over time the children will become used to working together, and a 'regular' partner will save you time when setting up the activities.

Generic activities

Many of the activities throughout this book follow common formats and structures. This will enable you to quickly set up and run a particular activity, and over time, the children will become used to the 'rules' involved. The 'generic' activities are described here in more detail.

Bingo

- The children work with their partners. They write several 'bingo' numbers on a piece of paper, circling each one. The numbers should match a certain criterion (e.g. less than 10).
- The teacher generates numbers at random (e.g. by selecting cards from a shuffled set).
- The teacher chooses a child to perform an operation on the card (e.g. saying the bond to make ten).
- The children can cross out one of their 'bingo' numbers if it matches the answer.
- The first pair to cross out all their numbers wins.

Match me

- The teacher has a set of number cards. Pupils have their own sets.
- Hold up a card. Read it aloud.
- Pupils perform some operation on the teacher's card and hold up the matching answer.

Missing numbers

- Write some sequences on the board, each with several numbers missing.
- Point to a missing number and choose one or several children to say which number it is.
- Repeat for each missing number.

Open the box

- Draw a grid on the board and write a number in each space.
- Cover each number with a piece of Blu-tacked card. Write a number on the card that relates in some way to the number beneath (e.g. 10 more, double).
- Select a child to choose a card and perform some operation on the number.
- Reveal the answer by removing the card.

Right and wrong

- Write several additions, subtractions, multiplications or divisions on the board, one or more of which are incorrect.
- The children work with their partners to decide which are incorrect.
- Allow a set time.
- For some activities you may wish to demonstrate a particular mental technique, before the children start the activity.
- Go through them on the board, asking different children whether each is correct or incorrect.

Round the class

- Write ten starter numbers on the board.
- Point to a number and say a child's name.
- That child performs some operation on the number and says the answer.
- If incorrect, choose another child.
- If correct, the first child chooses a second child and selects a new number.
- Continue like this around the class.

Grid operations

- Draw a grid on the board and write a number in each space.
- The children copy the empty grid, performing an operation on each number before entering it in their grid.
- Go through the grid on the board, asking different children for their answers.

Number match

- Ask the children to write a specific type of number on a piece of paper (e.g. 2-digit multiple of 10).
- Choose a child to select a number card at random and read it aloud.
- Write the number on the board.
- The children perform an operation on the number (e.g. multiply by 10).
- If the answer matches the number the children originally wrote down, then they can collect a cube.
- The first pair to collect three cubes wins.

Table timer

- On the board draw a table with three columns.
- Write some numbers in the left-hand column and two different operations above the middle and right-hand columns.
- The children copy the table, performing the operations and filling in the missing numbers.
- Time them to see how fast they can complete the table.

Target numbers

- Write a set of several numbers on the board, each in a triangle.
- Write another set of numbers on the board, each in a circle.
- The children use given operations to combine the triangle numbers to try to make the circle numbers.
- Allow a set time.
- Discuss the different answers.

Number cross

- Draw a cross on the board with three squares in each 'arm'.
- The children fill in the spaces with numbers so that the totals down and across fit a given pattern, e.g. the totals are equal, the total across is half the total down.
- Allow ten minutes.
- Discuss the different answers.

How many?

- Write a number on the board.
- The children have a given amount of time to find different ways of combining numbers and operations to make the target number.
- Discuss the different methods.

Four in a row

- Divide the class into four teams.
- Give each team a set of blank cards in a different colour.
- Point to numbers on a number grid and choose a child from one team to perform an operation.
- If correct, the team can cover a number on the number grid with a card of their colour.
- Repeat, choosing a child from each team in turn.
- The first team to complete a line of four cards in any direction wins.

Skills Chart

The following chart outlines all the mental skills addressed by the Mental Warm-up activities (the activities in the Activity Bank are listed separately, on pages 44 to 46).

The skills are divided into different areas: place-value and number, addition, subtraction, etc. The chart will assist any teacher looking for an activity dealing with a specific skill. It also makes clear the build-up and sequence of concepts covered throughout the book.

Specific skill	Unit
Place-value, ordering and rounding	
Place-value in 4-digit numbers	N1
Counting on in ones from a 4-digit number	N6
Counting in 50s	N6
Rounding 3-digit numbers to the nearest ten	N29
Rounding 3-digit numbers to the nearest hundred	N29
Estimating the result of adding two 3-digit numbers	N30
Recognising odd and even 4-digit numbers	N16, N34
Recognising the number one more/less than a negative number	N35
Ordering negative and positive numbers	N35
Fractions and decimals	
Finding thirds	N12
Finding eighths	N13
Finding fifths	N28
Fractions of an hour	N12
Equivalent fractions	N13
Ordering fractions	N27
Fractions of an hour	N28
Ordering decimal numbers	N40
Tenths	N40
Decimal fractions	N41
Adding 0·1 to a decimal number	N41

Addition and subtraction

Addition bonds to 10 and 20	N2
Addition bonds to 100	N4
Adding 100 to a 4-digit number	N1
Adding to make the next ten	N2, N3
Adding to make the next hundred	N32
Adding several 1-digit numbers	N5
Adding three 2-digit numbers	N17
Adding 19, 29	N14
Adding near multiples of 10	N14
Adding multiples of 10	N15, N17
Adding multiples of 100	N15
Adding a 3-digit and a 2-digit number	N30
Adding a multiple of 10 to a 3-digit number	N18
Adding a multiple of 100 to a 3-digit number	N18
Adding two amounts whose pence make £1 or £0·50	N43
Subtraction by counting on	N3, N19
Subtracting 2-digit numbers from multiples of 10	N20
Subtracting one 2-digit number from another	N20
Subtracting 100 from a 4-digit number	N16
Subtracting a multiple of 10 from a 3-digit number	N31
Subtracting multiples of 10	N31
Subtracting a 2-digit number from 50 or 100	N32
Subtracting 99, 199, 299, ...	N33
Subtracting one 3-digit number from another	N33, N42
Estimating and completing written subtractions	N42
Recognising addition and subtraction patterns	N34
Adding and subtracting amounts of money	N43
Finding change from 50p or £1	N19

Multiplication and division

Doubling numbers up to 100 (units less than 5)	N10
Doubling 2-digit multiples of 5	N10, N36
Doubling and adding	N36
Multiplying by 50 and 15	N7
Multiplication facts	N7, N23, N26, N39
Multiplying and adding	N9
Multiplying by 3 and 4	N9
Multiplication facts for 3, 4, 5, 6 and 10	N11
Multiplying by 4 and 8	N11
Multiples of 2, of 4 and of 8	N21
Multiplying by 2, 3, 4 and 5	N21
Multiplying by 3 and 6	N22
Multiplying by 9	N23
Multiplying by 7 and 14	N24
Multiplying by 7	N24
Multiplying by 10	N25
Multiplying by 100	N25
Multiplying 2-digit numbers	N26
Multiplying multiples of 10	N37
Multiplying 2-digit numbers	N37
Division facts	N8
Dividing with remainders	N38, N39

N1 Place-value

Grid addition

Adding 100 to a 4-digit number

Draw a 5×2 grid on the board, with a 4-digit number in each space. The children copy the grid, writing the number 100 more.

4646	2862	8693	5002	9197
7171	1628	3333	9906	8913

They should try to keep up with you as you write the numbers. When the grid is complete, point to each space in turn, asking a different child to say their answer.
Repeat, asking a child to write the original numbers.

Number match

Place-value in 4-digit numbers

Number cards (1 to 9)

Each pair writes a 4-digit number on a piece of paper. Choose a child to take a card at random and read it aloud. Write this number on the board. Each pair of children draws a Th H T U grid and writes the card number in one of the columns. They can use the number in the thousands, hundreds, tens or units column (or not at all) to try to build up the 4-digit number they originally wrote down. Repeat, choosing different children to take cards until one pair has made their 4-digit number.

Number of the week

Sample tasks

- Say a pair which add to make this number.
- Say the number which makes this number (20) with 7, 15, 9, ...
- Say a pair which multiply to make this number.

Sample facts

- It is 13 and 7, 4 and 16, ...
- It is half of 40, a quarter of 80, ...
- It is two 10s, four 5s, five 4s, ten 2s, ...
- It is the second multiple of 10.

N2 Addition/subtraction

Table timer

Addition bonds to 10 and 20

A timer

On the board draw a table with three columns. In the left-hand column write the numbers 1 to 9 at random. The children copy the table, writing the addition bonds to 10 in the middle column and to 20 in the right-hand column. Time them. How fast can they complete the table?

Bingo

Adding to make the next ten

Number cards (11 to 99, no multiples of 10)

Each pair writes five 1-digit bingo numbers.
Select a card at random, hold it up and say it aloud, e.g. 34.
If, by adding one of their bingo numbers to the card number, the children can make an answer which is a multiple of 10, they can cross out that bingo number, e.g. 34 + 6 = 40.

Word of the week

consecutive

Sample tasks

- Which number will make these **consecutive**: 8, 10, 11. 9 will make them **consecutive**.
- Are these **consecutive**: 33, 34, 35? Yes, they are consecutive.
- Three **consecutive** numbers have a total of 15. What are they? The **consecutive** numbers are 4, 5 and 6.

Sample facts

- **Consecutive** numbers are numbers in order.
- 3, 4 and 5 are **consecutive** numbers.
- 5, 7, 9 are **consecutive** odd numbers.

N3 Addition/subtraction

Grid addition

Adding to make the next ten

Draw a 5 × 2 grid on the board, with a 2-digit number in each space. The children copy the grid, writing the number that must be added to make the next 10. They should try to keep up with you as you write the numbers.
When the grid is complete, point to each space in turn, asking a different child to say their answer.

Bingo

Subtraction by counting on

Number cards (1 to 9)

Each pair writes five 1-digit bingo numbers.
Write two 2-digit numbers on the board and read them aloud, e.g. 29, 35.
If, by subtracting the smaller number from the larger number the children can make one of their bingo numbers, they can cross that number out, e.g. 35 − 29 = 6.

Number of the week

Sample tasks

- Say the multiples of 4, of 3, of 6, of 2, ... up to this number.
- Say a pair of numbers which multiply to make this number.
- Say a number which divides exactly into this number.

Sample facts

- Its digits are consecutive even numbers.
- It can be divided by 1, 2, 3, 4, 6, 8, 12, 24 – eight different numbers (it has eight factors).
- It is the number of hours in a day.

N4 Addition/subtraction

Team bingo

Addition bonds to 100

Number cards (5 to 95, multiples of 5 only)

Divide the class into five teams. Each team writes four bingo numbers that are multiples of 5 between 5 and 95. Write four numbers of your choice on the board.

Select a card at random, hold it up and read it aloud (e.g. 35).

Choose a child from one team to say its addition bond to 100 (i.e. 65). If a team has this matching number, they can cross it out.

Repeat, selecting another card and a child from the next team. Continue, choosing a child from each team in turn (including yourself as a team), maintaining a lively pace.

The first team to cross out all their bingo numbers wins. Can the class beat you?

Open the box

Addition bonds to 100

Draw a 5×2 grid on the board. Cover each space with a 2-digit number, and underneath write its bond to 100.

Choose a child to point to a box and say the addition bond to 100. Check with the class.

The child can 'open the box' to reveal the answer.

Shape of the week

Sample facts

- A **triangle** is a polygon with 3 sides.
- A **triangle** has 3 corners (vertices).
- A **triangle** has 3 angles.
- Cutting across a diagonal of a rectangle creates 2 identical (congruent) **triangles**.
- A pentagon can be divided into 3 **triangles**.

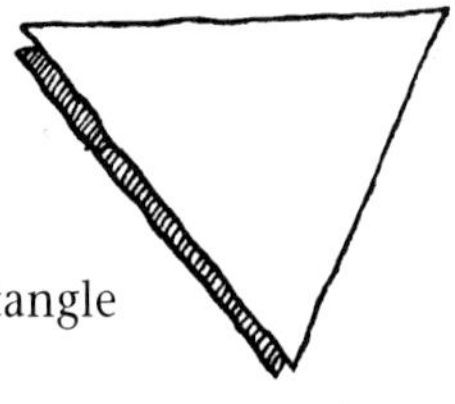

N5 Addition/subtraction

Number cross

Adding several 1-digit numbers

Number cards (1 to 9), one set per child

Draw a cross on the board with five squares in each 'arm'.
The children copy the grid and place the numbers 1 to 9 in the spaces so that the total down and across is the same. They can use number cards to help them.
Allow ten minutes, then discuss the different answers.

How many?

Adding several 1-digit numbers

Write a number on the board, e.g. 33.
The pairs work to find different ways of adding at least five 1-digit numbers to make the target number (e.g. 4 + 5 + 7 + 8 + 9 = 33).
Go round the class asking different pairs for their answers.

Number of the week

16

Sample tasks

- Say a double which makes this number.
- What is double this number?
- Say a number which divides exactly into this number.

Sample facts

- It is 4 × 4 – a square number.
- It is 4 less than 20, 14 less than 30, ...
- It is a multiple of 2, of 4, of 8, ...

N6 Properties of number

Open the box

Counting on in ones from a 4-digit number

Draw a 5 × 2 grid on the board. Cover each space with a 4-digit number, and underneath write the number that is 1 more.
Choose a child to point to a box and say the number that is 1 more. Check with the class.
The child can 'open the box' to reveal the answer.

Missing numbers

Counting in 50s

Write five sequences of numbers on the board, going up or down in 50s, each with several numbers missing (e.g. 33, 83, __, __, __, __, 333, __, __, 483, 533).
Point to a missing number and choose a child to say what it is. If that child is correct, they point to another missing number and choose another child to say what this is. Continue round the class.
Write in each missing number.

Word of the week

a fifth

Sample tasks

- How many **fifths** make a whole? Five **fifths** make a whole.
- What is a **fifth** of 20? A fifth of 20 is 4.
- How many tenths is the same fraction as one **fifth**? Two tenths matches one **fifth**.

Sample facts

- When a shape is divided into five equal parts, each one is one **fifth**.
- Two **fifths** are the same fraction as four tenths.
- A **fifth** of £1 is 20p.

N7 Multiplication/division

Table teaser

Multiplying by 50 and 15

Draw a table with three columns. In the left-hand column write the numbers 1 to 10 at random. In the bottom row, leave the left-hand column blank and write '1000' in the middle column and '300' in the right-hand column. The children copy the table, multiplying by 50 and writing the answer in the middle column, then multiplying by 15 and writing the answer in the right-hand column.
When they reach the bottom row, they must guess the number to be written in the left-hand column.

	x50	x15
3		
7		
4		
10		
8		
1		
5		
2		
6		
9		
	1000	300

Right and wrong

Multiplication facts

Write eight multiplications on the board, one of which is incorrect (e.g. $4 \times 40 = 160$, $5 \times 30 = 150$, $2 \times 16 = 32$, $3 \times 19 = 57$, $4 \times 60 = 240$, $5 \times 50 = 250$, $4 \times 16 = 54$, $8 \times 11 = 88$).
Allow the children five minutes to decide which multiplication is incorrect.

Number of the week

56

Sample tasks

- Add 14, 44, 24, ... to this number.
- Add 21, 32, 43, ... to this number.
- Say a pair of numbers which add to make this number.

Sample facts

- It is seven 8s.
- It is double 28.
- Its digits are consecutive.

N8 Multiplication/division

Four in a row

Division facts

Number grid (1 to 100), blank cards in three colours
Divide the class into three teams, and give each
team a set of blank cards.
On the grid, point to a number at random.
Choose a child in one team to give a division
fact about that number. *How many sixes in
eighteen?*

If the child answers correctly the team can cover the answer on the grid
with a card. Continue, choosing a child from each team in turn.
The winner is the first team to complete a line of four cards in any
direction.

Missing numbers

Division facts

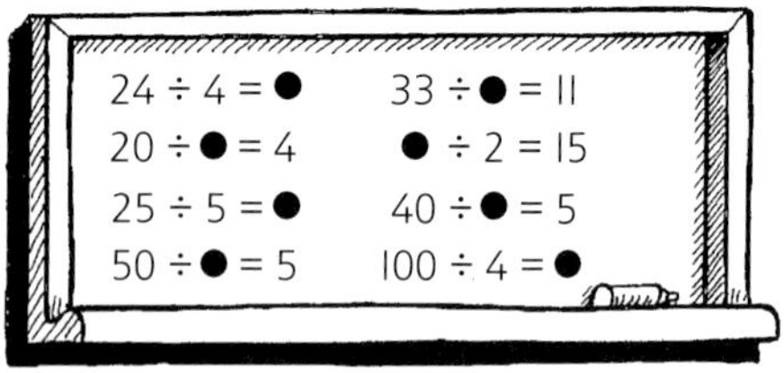

Write eight divisions on the
board, each with a missing
number.
Ask each pair to work out the
missing numbers.
Point to a missing number and
choose a pair to say what it is.
Repeat for each missing number.

24 ÷ 4 = ●	33 ÷ ● = 11
20 ÷ ● = 4	● ÷ 2 = 15
25 ÷ 5 = ●	40 ÷ ● = 5
50 ÷ ● = 5	100 ÷ 4 = ●

Shape of the week

Sample facts
- A **semicircle** is half of a circle.
- One side of a **semicircle** is the diameter of the circle.
- One half of a **semicircle** is a quarter-circle.
- A **semicircle** of paper can be folded into a cone.
- A **semicircle** is a symmetrical shape.

N9 Multiplication/division

How many?

Multiplying and adding

Write a number on the board, e.g. 70.
The pairs work to find different ways of multiplying two numbers and adding another to make the target (e.g. $6 \times 11 + 4$).
Go round the class asking different pairs for their answers.
Repeat for a different target number.

	x4	x3
5		
4		
10		
3		
20		
2		
6		
9		
1		

Table timer

Multiplying by 3 and 4

A timer

Draw a table with three columns. In the left-hand column write the numbers 1 to 6, 9, 10 and 20 at random.
Children copy the table, multiplying by 4 and writing the answer in the middle column, then multiplying by 3 and writing the answer in the right-hand column.
Time them. How quickly can they complete the table?

Number of the week

Sample tasks

- Add this number to 23, 45, 52, ... by adding 20, then subtracting 1.
- Subtract this number from 35, 67, 44, ... by subtracting 20, then adding 1.
- Say three numbers which total to make this number.

Sample facts

- It is 1 less than 20.
- It is the last odd number between 10 and 20.
- It can only be divided exactly by 1 or 19.

N10 Multiplication/division

Four in a row

Doubling numbers up to 100 (units less than 5)

Number grid (1 to 100), blank cards in four colours

Divide the class into four teams and give each team a set of blank cards.

Choose a child and point to a number on the grid (less than 50 and with fewer than 5 units). *Double this number.* If the child answers correctly the team can cover the answer on the grid with a card.

Continue, choosing a child from each team in turn.

The winner is the first team to complete a line of four cards in any direction.

Number match

Doubling 2-digit multiples of 5

Number cards (25 to 75, multiples of 5), cubes

Each pair writes a 2-digit multiple of 10 greater than 50 and less than 150 on a piece of paper. Choose a child to take a card at random and read it aloud, e.g. 35. Each pair doubles the number and writes down the answer, i.e. 70. If this number is the same as their original 2-digit multiple of 10, they claim a cube. Repeat choosing another child to take a different card. Continue until one pair has collected three cubes.

Word of the week

Sample tasks

- How many years make a **century**? A **century** is 100 years.
- What is ten **centuries**? Ten **centuries** make one thousand.
- What is one half a **century**? Fifty is one half a **century**.

Sample facts

- We are living in the twenty-first **century**.
- 25 is a quarter of a **century**.
- 'Cent' means 'one hundred, as in '**century**', 'centimetres', 'centipede', 'percentage'.

N11 Multiplication/division

Target numbers

Multiplication facts for 3, 4, 5, 6 and 10

On the board, write the numbers '3, 5, 10, 4, 6' each in a triangle, and the numbers '27, 20, 22, 90, 33' each in a circle. The children use addition and multiplication to combine any three of the triangle numbers to make a circle number. Allow ten minutes. Discuss the different answers.

Table timer

Multiplying by 4 and 8

A timer

Draw a table with three columns. In the left-hand column write the numbers 1 to 10 and 20 at random. The children copy the table, multiplying by 4 and writing the answer in the middle column, then multiplying by 8 (by doubling the previous answer) and writing the answer in the right-hand column. Divide the class into three teams. Which team can complete the table first?

	x4	x8
5		
4		
10		
3		
1		
7		
20		
2		
6		
9		
8		

Number of the week

12

Sample tasks

- Count in 3s (then 4s) forwards/backwards from this number.
- How many 2s/3s/4s/6s make this number?
- Continue halving from this number, i.e. 12, 6, 3, $1\frac{1}{2}$, ...

Sample facts

- It is double 6/four 3s/six 2s.
- It is a dozen, the number of months in a year, hours in the morning.
- Some of its multiples are 12, 24 and 36.

N12 Fractions/decimals

Target numbers

Finding thirds

Write '6, 9, 15, 30, 11, 12, 22' on the board, each in a square.
Write '33, 18, 66, 27, 50, 45, 90' on the board, each in a circle.
Point to a circle number and choose a child to say one third (choosing from the numbers in squares). If correct, that child can draw a line between the two numbers.
Repeat for each number. Which two have no matching partner?

Bingo

Fractions of an hour

Fraction cards ($\frac{1}{6}$, $\frac{2}{6}$, $\frac{1}{2}$, $\frac{4}{6}$, $\frac{5}{6}$, 1 whole)

Each pair writes five bingo numbers that are multiples of 10 up to 60.
Select a card at random, hold it up and read it aloud, e.g. two sixths.
Choose a child to say that fraction of one hour, i.e. 20 minutes.
Any pair with the matching number can cross it out.

prism

Shape of the week

Sample facts

- A **prism** is a 3-d shape.
- A **prism** has two identical ends.
- If the ends of the **prism** are triangles, then it is called a triangular **prism**.
- A prism with rectangular ends (rectangular **prism**) is called a cuboid.
- The faces on the sides of a **prism** are rectangles.

N13 Fractions/decimals

Grid fractions

Finding eighths

Draw a 5 × 2 grid on the board, with a different fraction (halves, quarters or sixteenths) in each space.

1	$\frac{2}{16}$	$\frac{1}{2}$	$\frac{1}{4}$	$\frac{3}{4}$
4	$\frac{4}{16}$	$\frac{2}{4}$	$\frac{12}{16}$	$\frac{14}{16}$

The children copy the grid, writing the matching number of eighths. When the grid is complete, point to each space in turn, asking a different child to say their answer.

Number cross

Equivalent fractions

Draw a cross on the board with three squares in each 'arm'. Write '$\frac{1}{2}$' in the central square.

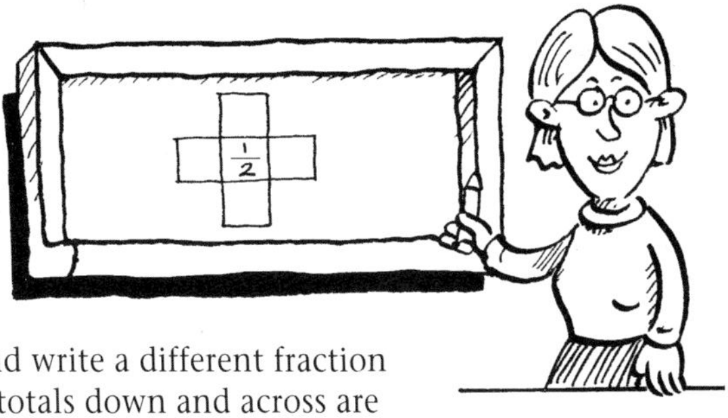

Children copy the grid and write a different fraction in each space so that the totals down and across are both 1.

Allow ten minutes, then discuss the different answers. Repeat for a 3 × 3 grid.

Number of the week

32

Sample tasks

- Count in 2s/4s/8s forwards/backwards to/from this number.
- How many 2s/4s/8s make this number?
- Continue halving from this number, i.e. 32, 16, 8, 4, 2, 1, $\frac{1}{2}$, $\frac{1}{4}$, ...
- What is a half/a quarter of this number?

Sample facts

- It is four 8s, eight 4s, two 16s.
- One quarter of it is 8.
- Its units digit is 1 less than its tens digit.

N14 Addition/subtraction

Grid addition

Adding 19, 29

Draw a 6 × 2 grid on the board, with a 2-digit number in each space.

25	18	34	39	52	47
36	47	43	28	71	55

The children copy the grid adding 19 to each number. When the grid is complete, point to each space in turn, asking a different child to say the answer.
Repeat for adding 29.

Right and wrong

Adding near multiples of 10

Write six additions on the board, two of which are incorrect. In pairs, allow the children five minutes to decide which are the incorrect additions.
Point to an addition and choose a child to say whether it is right or wrong. Repeat for each addition.

342 + 39 = 371 126 + 59 = 185
735 + 89 = 824 182 + 49 = 232
428 + 69 = 497 254 + 49 = 303

Word of the week

spherical

Sample tasks

- Show me an object that is **spherical**. The globe is **spherical**.
- Is this cube **spherical**? No, it is not **spherical**. It is not rounded like a ball.
- Mould this piece of plasticine to make **spherical** shape. My plasticine is now **spherical**.

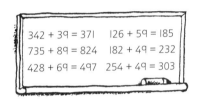

Sample facts

- **Spherical** means shaped like a sphere.
- A football is **spherical**.
- An egg is not **spherical**.

N15 Addition/subtraction

How many?

Adding multiples of 10

Write '1000' on the board.

The children find different ways of adding five multiples of 10 to make 1000, e.g. 200 + 180 + 220 + 140 + 260.

Allow ten minutes. Discuss the different answers.

Repeat for making 340 from four consecutive multiples of 10.

Number match

Adding multiples of 100

Number cards (1 to 9), cubes

Each pair writes a multiple of 100 between 1000 and 2000 on a piece of paper. Choose a child to pick a number card at random and say it aloud, e.g. 6. Write this number of hundreds on the board, i.e.'600'. Replace the card at the bottom of the pile and select a different child to pick another card. Continue until one pair can add some of the multiples to make the number they wrote down originally. Repeat with the children writing new multiples of 100.

Number of the week

81

Sample tasks

- Count in 9s forwards/backwards to/from this number
- What must be added to this number to make 100?
- Subtract 30, 50, 20, 40, ... from this number

Sample facts

- It is nine 9s – a square number.
- Its nearest 10 is 80.
- Its digits differ by 7 – one odd and one even digit.

N16 Place-value

Number match

Recognising odd and even 4-digit numbers

Number cards (1 to 9), cubes

Each pair writes a 4-digit number on a piece of paper. Choose a child to pick a card at random and say it aloud, e.g. 6. Write this number on the board. Each pair of children draws a Th H T U grid and writes the card number in one of the columns. They can use the number in the thousands, hundreds, tens or units column (or not at all) to try to build up the 4-digit number they originally wrote down. Repeat, choosing different children to take cards until one pair has made their 4-digit number. If they can identify whether their number is odd or even, they may collect a cube. Repeat until one pair has collected three cubes.

Grid addition

Subtracting 100 from a 4-digit number

Draw a 5 × 2 grid on the board, with a 4-digit number in each space. The children copy the grid, writing the numbers 100 less. When the grid is complete, point to each space in turn, asking a different child to say their answer.

4862	3173	1959	6114	9009
7597	8043	3100	4108	5555

Shape of the week

polygon

Sample facts

- A **polygon** is a 2-d shape with straight sides.
- A **polygon** with 3 sides is called a triangle.
- A **polygon** with 6 sides is called a hexagon.
- A rectangle is a 4-sided **polygon**.
- A **polygon** with equal sides and angles is called a regular **polygon**.

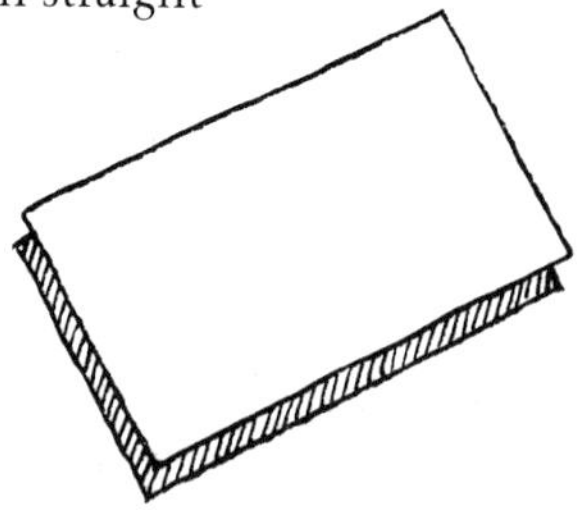

N17 Addition/subtraction

Number cross

Adding multiples of 10

Draw a cross on the board with five squares in each 'arm'. Write the numbers '20, 30, 40, 50, 60' next to the cross.

The children copy the grid and place the numbers 20 to 60 in the spaces on the vertical arm.

They write numbers in the horizontal arm so that the total across is half the total down.

Allow ten minutes, then discuss the different answers.

How many?

Adding three 2-digit numbers

Write a number on the board, e.g. 78.

The pairs work to find different ways of adding three 2-digit numbers to make the target number, e.g. 36 + 29 + 13. Give a special prize to any pair that finds the way that involves adding three consecutive numbers, i.e. 25 + 26 + 27.

Discuss the different answers.

Number of the week

Sample tasks

- Colour this fraction of a strip of 5 squares. How many squares are coloured?
- Colour this fraction of a strip of 10 squares. How many squares are coloured? How many are not coloured?
- If a square grid is 3 × 5, and we coloured this fraction, how many squares would we colour?

Sample facts

- With $\frac{2}{5}$ it makes a whole.
- It is 3 lots of one fifth.
- The top and bottom parts of the fraction are both odd.

N18 Addition/subtraction

Grid addition

Adding a multiple of 10 to a 3-digit number

Draw a 5 × 2 grid on the board, with a 3-digit number in each space.
The children copy the grid, writing the numbers that are 40 more.
When the grid is complete, point to each space in turn, asking a different child to say their answer.
Repeat for adding 20, 30, 50, ...

Closest to 1000

Adding a multiple of 100 to a 3-digit number

Number cards (0 to 9)

Each pair writes a 3-digit number on their paper.
Select a card at random, multiply it by 100 and say the answer aloud, e.g. for 3, say three hundred. Each pair adds or subtracts that number to their starting number. Go round the class, asking each pair for their answer.
The pair who are closest to 1000 win.

Word of the week

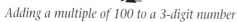

Sample tasks

- What is the **remainder** when 7 is divided by 3? When 7 is divided by 3, there is a **remainder** of 1.
- Tell me a division which has a **remainder** of 2. 12 divided by 5 leaves a **remainder** of 2.
- Which numbers leave no **remainder** when divided by 5? Numbers which leave no **remainder** are 5, 10, 15, 20, ...

Sample facts

- A **remainder** is what is left over after dividing.
- Odd numbers leave a **remainder** of 1 when divided by 2.
- When divided by 3 numbers either divide exactly, or leave a **remainder** of 1 or 2.

N19 Addition/subtraction

Bingo

Finding change from 50p or £1

Number cards (1 to 50)

Each pair writes three 2-digit bingo numbers (less than 50). Select a card at random, hold it up and say it aloud. Choose a child to say how much change from 50p there would be if they bought an item at this price. Any pair with the matching number can cross it out.
Repeat for change from £1, using number cards 1 to 100.

Four in a row

Subtraction by counting on

Number grid (1 to 100), blank cards in four colours

Divide the class into four teams, and give each team a set of coloured blank cards.
Point to two 2-digit numbers on the grid, e.g. 38 and 66. Choose a child to say the difference between the two numbers. If the child answers correctly the team can cover either of the first two numbers on the grid with a card of their colour.
Continue, choosing a child from each team in turn.
The winner is the first team to complete a line of four cards in any direction.

Number of the week

Sample tasks

- How many quarters, eighths, ... in this number?
- Is this number more or less than $\frac{1}{3}$, $\frac{3}{4}$, ...?
- Say four fractions which match (are equivalent to) this number.

Sample facts

- It matches two quarters, three sixths, four eighths.
- It is the result of dividing something exactly by 2.
- It is more than $\frac{1}{4}$, $\frac{1}{3}$, $\frac{2}{5}$ and less than $\frac{3}{4}$, $\frac{4}{5}$.

N20 Addition/subtraction

Open the box

Subtracting 2-digit numbers from multiples of 10

Draw a 5 × 2 grid on the board. Cover each space with a subtraction of a 2-digit number from a larger multiple of 10, e.g. 80 – 34, and underneath write the answer.

Choose a child to point to a box and say the answer. Check with the class.

The child can 'open the box' to reveal the answer.

Number match

Subtracting one 2-digit number from another

Number cards (10 to 50)

Each pair writes a 2-digit number less than 40 on a piece of paper. Choose a child to pick two cards at random and say them aloud, e.g. 12 and 38. Each pair of children subtracts the smaller from the larger and writes down the answer. Replace the cards and repeat, choosing different children to take cards until one pair has made their original 2-digit number.

Shape of the week **square-based pyramid**

Sample facts

- A pyramid with a square base is called a **square-based pyramid**.
- A **square-based pyramid** has 5 faces.
- The sloping faces of a **square-based pyramid** are triangular.
- The faces of a **square-based pyramid** are 4 triangles and 1 square.
- A **square-based pyramid** has 5 vertices, 5 faces and 8 edges.

N21 Properties of number

Table timer

Multiples of 2, of 4 and of 8

A timer

Draw a table with four columns. In the left-hand column write the numbers 1 to 12 in order.
The children copy the table, multiplying by 2 and writing the answer in the first empty column, then multiplying by 4 and writing the answer in the next column and finally multiplying by 8 and writing the answer in the right-hand column. How quickly can they complete the table?

Target numbers

Multiplying by 2, 3, 4 and 5

Write '14, 6, 9, 4, 7' on the board, each in a triangle.
Write '70, 82, 150, 44, 52, 68' on the board, each in a circle.
The children choose three of the triangle numbers, multiplying each by 2, 3, 4 or 5 and finding the total of the answers. Can they make any of the circle numbers?
E.g. $14 \times 2 = 28$, $4 \times 3 = 12$, $6 \times 5 = 30$, $28 + 12 + 30 = 70$.
Allow ten minutes.
Discuss the different answers.

Number of the week

2·4

Sample tasks

- Say this number as a fraction
- How many tenths are in this number?
- What must be added to this number to make 3?

Sample facts

- It is two wholes and four tenths of a whole.
- It is between 2 and 3.
- It is the same as 24 tenths, or one whole and 14 tenths.

N22 Multiplication/division

Number match

Multiplying by 3 and 6

Number cards (1 to 9), cubes

Each pair writes a 2-digit multiple of 6 on a piece of paper. Choose a child to pick a card at random (e.g. 5) and multiply the number by 3 (i.e. 15). Choose another child to double their answer (30) and write the total as a x6 table fact, i.e. '5 × 6 = 30'. You write this number on the board. Any pair that wrote down that multiple of 6 on their paper can collect a cube. Repeat, with the children writing new multiples of 6 each time, until one pair has collected four cubes.

Bingo

Multiplying by 3 and 6

Number cards (1 to 12)

Each pair writes five bingo numbers that are multiples of 3 or 6. Select a card at random, hold it up and say it aloud. Choose a child to multiply by 3 or 6 (you decide). Any pair with a matching number can cross it out.

Word of the week

square centimetre

Sample tasks

- If a rectangle measures 4 cm by 3 cm, how many **square centimetres** are inside? Its area is 12 square centimetres.
- If a rectangle has an area of 10 **square centimetres**, what shape could the rectangle be? 1 × 10 and 2 × 5 rectangles each have areas of 10 **square centimetres**.

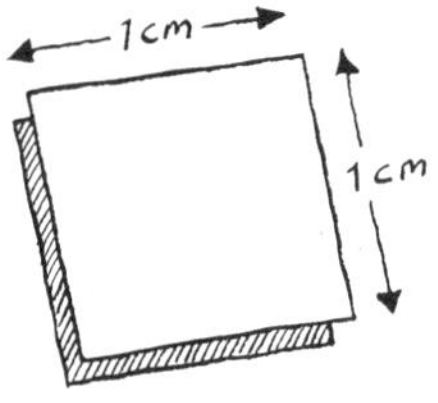

- On cm-squared paper, draw a shape which has an area of 15 **square centimetres**. This 3 × 5 rectangle has an area of 15 **square centimetres**.

Sample facts

- A **square centimetre** is a square whose sides are 1 centimetre long.
- A **square centimetre** is a unit used for measuring area.
- A square of side 4 cm has an area of 16 **square centimetres**.

N23 Multiplication/division

Grid multiplication

Multiplying by 9

Draw a 6 × 2 grid on the board, with a number from 1 to 12 in each space (include 20 also).
The children copy the grid, writing the matching multiple of 9 in each space.
When the grid is complete, point to each space in turn, asking a different child to say their answer.
Repeat for multiplying by 6, 7, 8, ...

Four in a row

Multiplication facts

Number grid (1 to 100), blank cards in four colours

Divide the class into four teams, and give each team a set of coloured blank cards.
Point to a 2-digit number on the board, e.g. 45.
Choose a child to say a multiplication that has this number as its answer, e.g. 5 × 9.
If the child answers correctly their team can cover that 2-digit number, i.e. 45, on the grid with a card of their colour.
Continue, choosing a child from each team in turn.
The winner is the first team to complete a line of four cards in any direction.

Number of the week

1·5

Sample tasks

- Say a number which is more/less than this number.
- What is four tenths, seven tenths, ... more/less than this number?
- What must be added to this number to make 2, 3, 5, 10, ...?

Sample facts

- It is one whole and five tenths.
- It is exactly halfway between 1 and 2.
- It is one half of 3.

N24 Multiplication/division

Table timer

Multiplying by 7 and 14

A timer

Draw a table with three columns. In the left-hand column write numbers 1 to 12 at random. Children copy the table, multiplying by 7 and writing the answer in the middle column, then multiplying by 14 and writing the answer in the right-hand column. How fast can they complete the table?

Number cross

Multiplying by 7

Draw a cross on the board with three squares in each 'arm'.
The children copy the grid and write 1- or 2-digit numbers in the spaces, so that the totals across and down are both multiples of 7.
Allow ten minutes, then discuss the different answers.

Shape of the week

pentagon

Sample facts

- A **pentagon** is a 2-d shape.
- A **pentagon** is a polygon with 5 sides.
- A **pentagon** can be divided into 3 triangles.
- A **pentagon** has one less side than a hexagon.
- A pyramid with a pentagonal base is called a **pentagonal** pyramid.

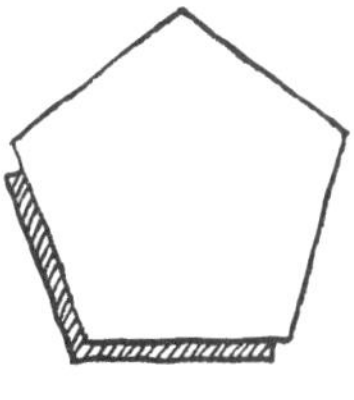

N25 Multiplication/division

Right and wrong

Multiplying by 10

Write eight multiplications of 3-digit numbers by 10 on the board, two of which are incorrect.
Allow the children five minutes to decide which multiplications are incorrect.

$352 \times 10 = 3520$ $819 \times 10 = 8190$
$954 \times 10 = 9540$ $202 \times 10 = 2020$
$760 \times 10 = 7060$ $700 \times 10 = 7000$
$478 \times 10 = 4780$ $350 \times 10 = 3505$

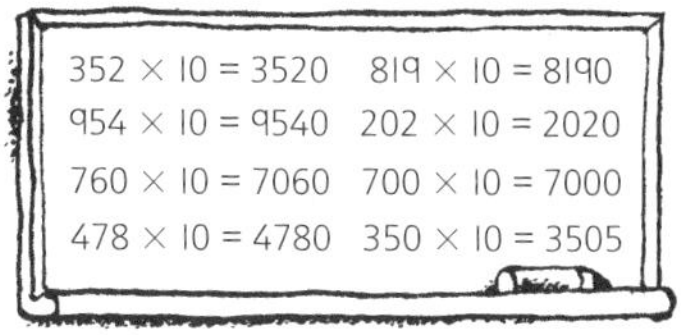

Open the box

Multiplying by 100

Draw a 5×2 grid on the board. Cover each space with a 2-digit number, and underneath write that number multiplied by 100.
Choose a child to point to a box and multiply by 100.
Check with the class.
The child can 'open the box' to reveal the answer.

Number of the week

10

Sample tasks
- Multiply 23, 15, 46, 9, 58, ... by this number.
- What has this number been multiplied by to make 450, 80, 170, ...?
- Divide 340, 200, 190, ... by this number.

Sample facts
- When you multiply by this number, all the digits slide one place left.
- When you divide by this number, all the digits slide one place right.
- It is the number of millimetres in a centimetre.
- It is the first 2-digit number.

N26 Multiplication/division

Grid multiplication

Multiplication facts

Draw a 5 × 2 grid on the board, with numbers 2 to 10 and 20 in the spaces.

4	3	8	6	2
5	9	7	10	20

Children copy the grid, writing the matching multiple of 22 in each space.
When the grid is complete, point to each space in turn, asking a different child to say their answer.

How many?

Multiplying 2-digit numbers

Write a number on the board, e.g. 78.
The pairs work to find different ways of multiplying a 2-digit number to make the target number, e.g. 2 × 39, 3 × 26, 6 × 13. Give a special prize to any pair that finds all three ways.
Discuss the different answers.
Repeat with a different target number, e.g. 64.

fraction

Word of the week

Sample tasks

- If a whole shape is divided into 3 equal parts, what **fraction** is each part? Each fraction is one third.
- Which **fraction** is larger, one third or one quarter? One third is the larger **fraction**.
- In a group of 10 children, 7 are girls. What **fraction** are boys? The **fraction** that are boys is three tenths.

Sample facts

- A **fraction** is a part of a whole.
- The **fraction** one half is the same as the fraction two quarters.
- One half of one quarter is the **fraction** one eighth.

N27 Fractions/decimals

Grid fractions

Ordering fractions

Draw a 5 × 2 grid on the board and write a different fraction in each space (halves, quarters, thirds, fifths, sixths or eighths).
The children copy the grid writing smaller fractions in the top row and larger fractions in the bottom row.
When the grid is complete, point to each space in turn, asking a different child to say their answer. Discuss the different possible answers.

Number cross

Ordering fractions

Draw a cross on the board with 3 squares in each 'arm'. Write '$\frac{1}{2}$' in the central square.
Children copy the grid and write a different fraction in each space so that the fractions increase in size from top to bottom and from left to right.
Allow ten minutes, then discuss the different answers.

Number of the week

Sample tasks

- Read this number.
- How many units, tens, hundreds, thousands in this number?
- Count forwards/backwards in ones from this number.
- Count forwards/backwards in tens/hundreds from this number.

Sample facts

- It is between 5000 and 6000.
- Its nearest ten is 5330, its nearest hundred is 5300.
- The total of its digits is 16.

N28 Fractions/decimals

Target numbers

Finding fifths

Write 6, 9, 15, 30, 18, 12, 36 on the board, each in a square.
Write 20, 15, 10, 25, 50, 35, 60 on the board, each in a circle.
Point to a circle number and choose a child to say three fifths of it (choosing from the numbers in squares). If correct, the child can draw a line between the two numbers.
Allow five minutes for each pair to copy the numbers and to match each circle number to the square number that is three fifths of it.
Check each number. Which two have no matching partner?

Bingo

Fractions of an hour

Fraction cards ($\frac{1}{6}$, $\frac{1}{3}$, $\frac{1}{2}$, $\frac{2}{3}$, $\frac{5}{6}$, 1 whole)

Each pair writes five bingo numbers that are multiples of 10 up to 60.
Select a card at random, hold it up and say it aloud, e.g. one sixth.
Choose a child to say that fraction of one hour, i.e. 10 minutes.
Any pair with the matching number can cross it out.

Shape of the week

tetrahedron

Sample facts

- A **tetrahedron** is a regular 3-d shape.
- A triangular pyramid is called a **tetrahedron**.
- A **tetrahedron** has 4 triangular faces.
- A **tetrahedron** has 4 vertices, and 6 edges.
- More than one **tetrahedron** are called **tetrahedra**.

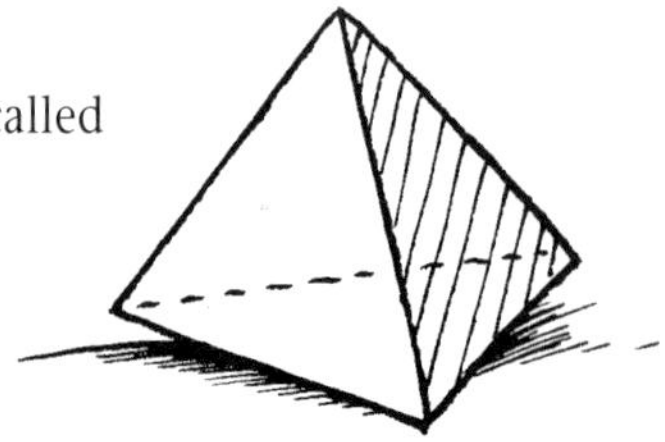

N29 Place-value

Missing numbers

Rounding 3-digit numbers to the nearest ten

Write ten 3-digit numbers on the board, and a blank box next to each.
Point to a number, and choose a child to say the nearest ten.
Check with the class. If correct, that child can write the answer in the appropriate box.
Continue, for each number.

Bingo

Rounding 3-digit numbers to the nearest hundred

Number cards (0 to 9)

Each pair writes five 3-digit bingo numbers.
Select a card at random, multiply it by 100 and say the number aloud, e.g. for 3, say *three hundred.*
Any pair with a number that will round to that multiple of 100 can cross it out.

Number of the week

Sample tasks

- How many units, tens, hundreds in this number?
- Round this number to its nearest ten/hundred. How far is it away?
- Count forwards/backwards in units/tens/hundreds from this number.

Sample facts

- It is between 460 and 470.
- It is double 234.
- Its digits are consecutive even numbers.

N30 Addition/subtraction

Open the box

Estimating the result of adding two 3-digit numbers
Draw a 5 × 2 grid on the board. Cover each space with the addition of two 3-digit numbers and underneath write the approximate answer by rounding each number to the nearest ten or hundred.
Choose a child to point to a box and estimate the total.
Check with the class. The child can 'open the box' to reveal the estimate. How close are the two estimates?

Missing numbers

Adding a 3-digit and a 2-digit number
Write ten additions of 3- and 2-digit numbers on the board. Replace one or two digits of the answer with letters. Point to a letter and choose a child to say what digit it represents. Repeat for each letter.

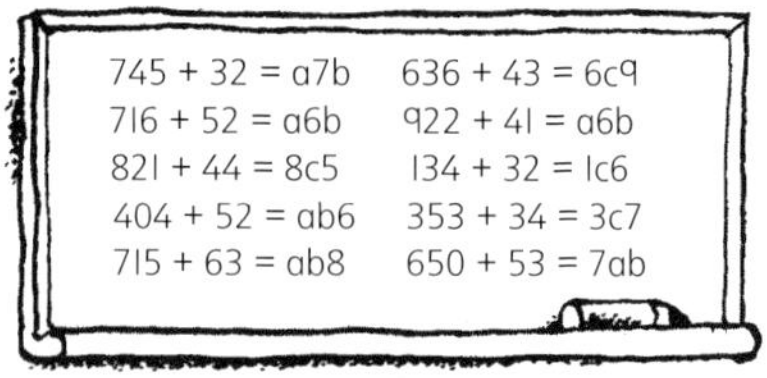

Word of the week

perimeter

Sample tasks

- What is the **perimeter** of a square with sides 3 cm long? Its **perimeter** is four 3s, which is 12 centimetres.

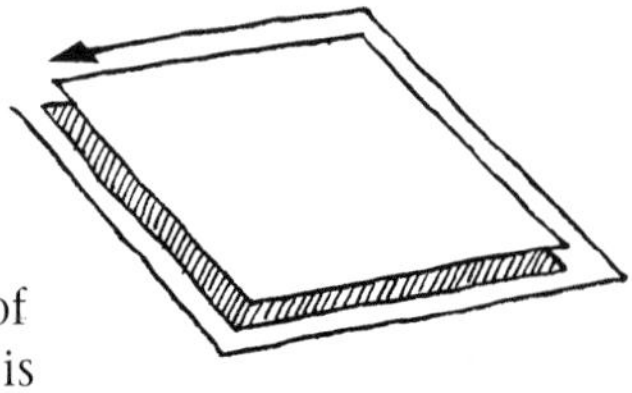

- A square has a **perimeter** of 24 centimetres. How long is each side of the square? If its **perimeter** is 24 cm, then its sides are 6 cm long.
- Measure the **perimeter** of this rectangle. Its **perimeter** is 14 cm.

Sample facts

- The **perimeter** of a shape is the distance around its boundary.
- A 3 cm × 5 cm rectangle has a **perimeter** of 16 cm.
- A 4 × 4 square and a 3 × 5 rectangle each have the same **perimeter**.

N31 Addition/subtraction

Right and wrong

Subtracting a multiple of 10 from a 3-digit number

Write six subtractions of multiples of 10 from 3-digit numbers on the board, some of which are incorrect.
Allow the children five minutes to decide which subtractions are incorrect.

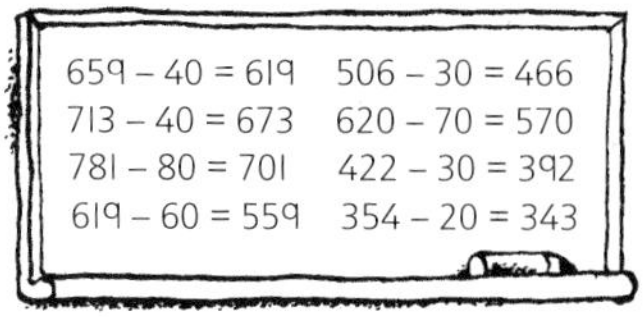

Target numbers

Subtracting multiples of 10

Write 76, 38, 41, 63, 55 on the board, each in a triangle.
Write 163, 73, 223 on the board, each in a circle.
The children subtract different multiples of 10 from the triangle numbers. Can they add two or more of their answers to make any of the circle numbers?
Allow ten minutes.
Discuss the different answers.

Number of the week

Sample tasks

- Count in ones/twos to/from this number.
- Say an odd and an even number which add to make this number. Can you say two odds? Or two evens?
- What must be added to this number to make an odd/even number?

Sample facts

- It is the eighth odd number.
- It is one half of 30, one third of 45, one quarter of 60.
- It is the third multiple of 5, the first multiple of 15.

N32 Addition/subtraction

Bingo

Subtracting a 2-digit number from 50 or 100

Number cards (1 to 50)

Each pair writes five 2-digit bingo numbers that are less than 50.
Select a card at random, hold it up and read it aloud. Choose a child to say how much change from 50p there would be if they bought an item at this price. Any pair with the matching number can cross it out.
Repeat for change from £1, using number cards 1 to 100.

Open the box

Adding to make the next hundred

Draw a 5 × 2 grid on the board. Cover each space with a 3-digit number, and underneath write what must be added to make the next hundred. Allow five to ten minutes for the pairs to work out the numbers hidden in each box.
Choose a child to point to a box. They say the next hundred and what must be added to make it. Check with the class.
The child can 'open the box' to reveal the answer.

Shape of the week

hemisphere

Sample facts

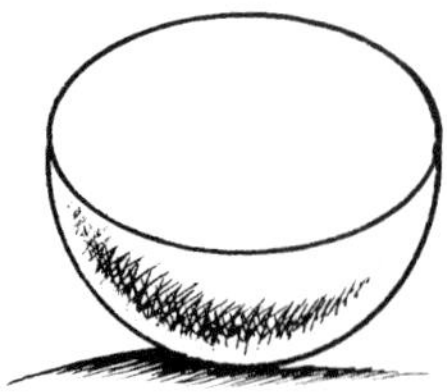

- A **hemisphere** is half of a sphere.
- A **hemisphere** is a 3-d shape which is hollow or solid.
- A **hemisphere** has one curved face and one flat face (a circle).
- If an object is shaped like half a sphere, e.g. a bowl, it is called **hemispherical**.
- The shape of half of an orange is a **hemisphere**.

Addition/subtraction

Bingo

Subtracting 99, 199, 299, ...

Number cards (0 to 9)

Each pair writes ten 3-digit bingo numbers.
Select three cards at random to make a 3-digit number. On the board, write the subtraction of 99, 199, 299, ... (you decide) from the card number.
Choose a child to say the answer.
Any pair with a matching number can cross it out. The winner is the first pair to cross out two numbers.

Right and wrong

Subtracting one 3-digit number from another

Write eight subtractions of two 3-digit numbers on the board, one of which is incorrect.

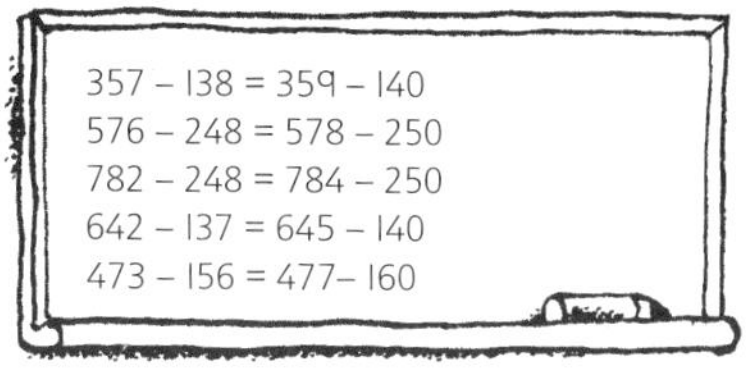

Allow the children five minutes to decide which subtraction is incorrect.

Number of the week

Sample tasks

- Continue doubling from this number (4, 8, 16, 32, 64, ...)
- What must be added to this number to make 60, 30, 80, 140, ...?
- Multiply this number by 7, 3, 5, 9, ...

Sample facts

- It is the second even number.
- It is 2×2 – it is a square number.
- It is the number of seasons in a year, quarters in a whole.

N34 Properties of number

Open the box

Recognising odd and even 4-digit numbers

Draw a 5 × 2 grid on the board. Cover each space with a 4-digit number and underneath write 'odd' or 'even'. Allow a few minutes for the pairs to decide whether each number is odd or even.

Choose a child to point to a box and say odd or even. Check with the class.The child can 'open the box' to reveal the answer.

Odd and even teams!

Recognising addition and subtraction patterns

Divide the class into two teams, odd and even. Each pair writes a subtraction and an addition with answers that are their type of number (i.e. odd or even). Give the teams one point for every correct calculation with an odd or even answer as appropriate. If more than one pair writes the same calculation the team loses a point.

Word of the week

coordinates

Sample tasks

- Look at this point on the grid. What are its **coordinates**? Its **coordinates** are (3, 5).
- Mark the point whose **coordinates** are (4, 4). This point has **coordinates** (4, 4).
- What are the **coordinates** of the vertices of this triangle? Its **coordinates** are (1, 3), (3, 5), (0, 6).

Sample facts

- **Coordinates** mark positions of points on a square grid.
- The first **coordinate** is the distance 'along', the second **coordinate** is the distance 'up'.
- If the first **coordinate** is zero, then the point lies on the vertical axis. If the second **coordinate** is zero, then the point lies on the horizontal axis.

N35 Properties of number

Grid addition

Recognising the number one more/less than a negative number

Draw a 5 × 2 grid on the board, with a negative number in each space.

−5	−10	−2	−11	−100
−1	−9	−20	−13	−1000

The children copy the grid, writing the numbers that are 1 more. Remind them that these numbers are negative. (You may need to do some examples with those children who find this difficult.)
When the grid is complete, point to each space in turn, asking a different child to say the answer.
Repeat for one less.

Missing numbers

Ordering negative and positive numbers

Write five sequences of negative and positive numbers on the board, each with several numbers missing.
Point to a missing number and choose a child to say what it is.
Repeat for each missing number.

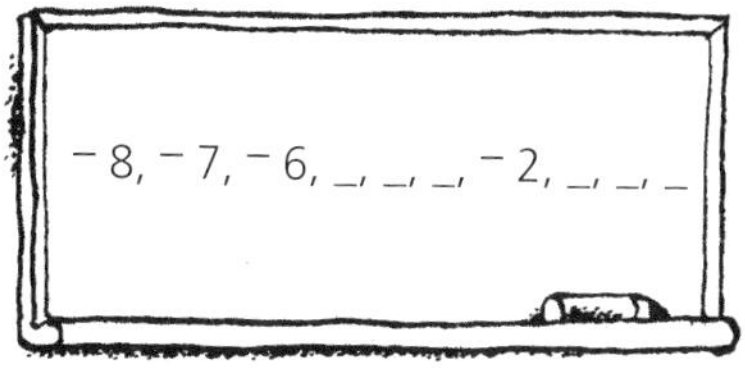

Number of the week

Sample tasks

- What must be added to this number to make the next ten?
- Subtract this number from 30, 70, 40, ...
- Subtract this number from 31, 72, 43, ...

Sample facts

- It is two 9s, three 6s, six 3s, nine 2s, eighteen 1s.
- It makes 50 with 32, 70 with 52, 100 with 82.
- It is one and a half dozen.

N36 Multiplication/division

Bingo

Doubling 2-digit multiples of 5

Each pair writes five bingo numbers that are multiples of 10 (up to 200).
Say a multiple of 5 (up to 100).
Choose a child to double your number and say the answer.
Any pair with the matching number can cross it out.

How many?

Doubling and adding

Write a number on the board, e.g. 550.
The pairs work to find different ways of doubling a number and adding another to make the target, e.g. double 250 add 50.
Discuss the different answers.
Repeat with a new target number.

Shape of the week

octagon

Sample facts

- An **octagon** is a 2-d shape.
- An **octagon** is an 8-sided polygon.
- An **octagon** has 8 vertices.
- An **octagon** has twice as many sides as a square.
- An **octagon** has 3 more vertices than a pentagon.

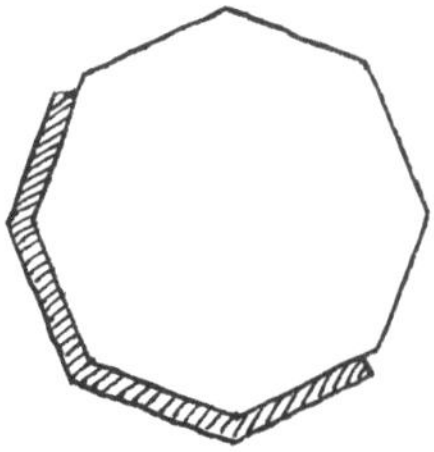

N37 Multiplication/division

Number match

Multiplying multiples of 10

Number cards (10, 20, 30, ... 100), cubes

Each pair writes four multiples of 10 between 80 and 800 on a piece of paper. Choose a child to pick a card at random and say the number, e.g. 30. Write this number on the board. Each pair multiplies the number by 4 and writes down the answer. Any pair that wrote this multiple of 10 on their paper originally can claim a cube. Replace the card and repeat, choosing a different child to take another card. Continue until one pair has collected two cubes.

Table timer

Multiplying 2-digit numbers

A timer

Draw a table with three columns. In the left-hand column write the numbers 0 to 9 at random. In pairs, the children copy the table, multiplying each number by 13 and writing the answer in the middle column, then multiplying each number by 25 and writing the answer in the right-hand column. Encourage a wide use of different mental methods (e.g. doubling, halving, multiplying by 10 and subtracting,...).

	13	25
5		
4		
20		
3		
8		
2		
6		
11		
9		

Number of the week

7

Sample tasks

- Count in 7s forwards from 0 to 70 and backwards from 70 to 0.
- Multiply this number by 9, 4, 10, 5, ...
- How many times does this number divide into 21, 35, 70, ...?

Sample facts

- It is the fourth odd number.
- It is one half of 14, one third of 21.
- It is the number of days in a week, colours in a rainbow.

N38 Multiplication/division

Bingo

Dividing with remainders

Each pair writes five 1-digit bingo numbers.
Write a division of a 2-digit by a 1-digit number on the board.
Choose a child to say the answer and any remainder.
Any pair with a number that matches the remainder can cross it out.

Number cross

Dividing with remainders

Draw a cross on the board with three squares in each 'arm'.
Children copy the grid and write 2-digit numbers in the spaces.
Can they place the numbers so that when they are divided by 5, the sum of their remainders is the same across and down?
Allow ten minutes, then discuss the different answers.

Word of the week

Sample tasks

- Estimate the capacity of this jug in **millilitres**.
  I estimate that it will hold 700 **millilitres**.
- Measure the capacity of this pot in **millilitres** by pouring into the measuring jug. Its capacity is nearly 400 **millilitres**.
- How many **millilitres** match half a litre? Half a litre is the same as 500 **millilitres**.

Sample facts

- A **millilitre** is a measure of capacity.
- 1000 **millilitres** is the same capacity as 1 litre.
- This measuring jug is marked in 100 **millilitres**.

N39 Multiplication/division

Grid multiplication

Multiplication facts

Draw a 6 × 2 grid on the board, with a number from 30 to 99 in each space. The children copy the grid, dividing each number by 3 and writing the remainder in each space.

47	91	78	65	82	56
38	77	83	100	98	200

When the grid is complete, point to each space in turn, asking a different child to say their answer.

Repeat for dividing by 5. Do children see the patterns? Do they have to do the divisions to write the remainder?

Number match

Dividing with remainders

Number cards (1 to 9)

Each pair writes a 1-digit number between 1 and 8 on a piece of paper. Write a 2-digit number on the board, e.g. 47. Choose a child to pick a card at random and read it aloud. The children divide the number on the board by the card number and write down the remainder. Any pair who originally wrote down a number that matches the remainder can collect a cube. Replace the card and repeat, writing a new 2-digit number on the board and choosing a different child to take another card. Who collects the most cubes? *What remainder numbers come up most? Are some numbers better numbers than others to write on your piece of paper?*

Number of the week

100

Sample tasks

- What must be added to 30, 60, 10, 80, ... to make this number?
- What must be added to 25, 45, 62, 91, ... to make this number?
- Add this number to 345, 762, 703, ...

Sample facts

- It is 10 × 10 – it is a square number.
- It is the number of centimetres in a metre.
- It is the number of years/runs in a century.

N40 Fractions/decimals

Missing numbers

Ordering decimal numbers
Write five sequences of decimal numbers on the board, each with several numbers missing.
Point to a missing number and choose a child to say what it is.
Repeat for each missing number.

1·5 1·6 _ 1·8 _ 2·0 2·1

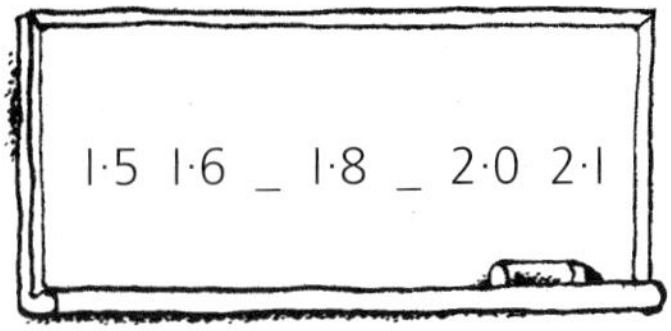

Right and wrong

Tenths
On the board write ten decimals and their fraction equivalents, some of which are incorrect.
Allow the children five minutes to decide which are incorrect.

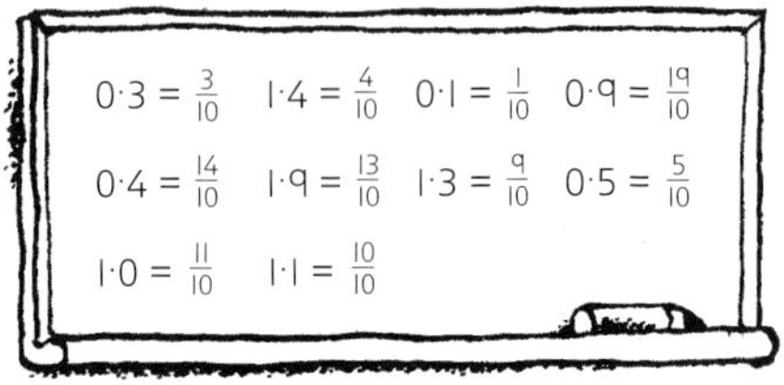

$0.3 = \frac{3}{10}$ $1.4 = \frac{4}{10}$ $0.1 = \frac{1}{10}$ $0.9 = \frac{19}{10}$

$0.4 = \frac{14}{10}$ $1.9 = \frac{13}{10}$ $1.3 = \frac{9}{10}$ $0.5 = \frac{5}{10}$

$1.0 = \frac{11}{10}$ $1.1 = \frac{10}{10}$

Shape of the week

heptagon

Sample facts
- A **heptagon** is a 2-d shape.
- A **heptagon** is a 7-sided polygon.
- A **heptagon** has 7 vertices.
- A **heptagon** has 1 more side than a hexagon and 1 less than an octagon.
- 'Hept' means seven – a heptathlete competes in 7 events.

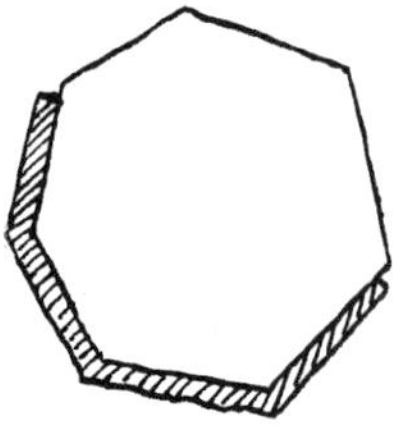

N41 Fractions/decimals

Four in a row

Decimal fractions

Number cards (0 to 9), blank cards in four colours

Draw a 10 × 4 grid on the board, numbered 0·1, 0·2, 0·3, ... along the top row, 1·1, 1·2, 1·3, ... along the next row, 2·1, 2·2, 2·3, ... along the next row, and 3·1, 3·2, 3·3, ... along the bottom row.

Divide the class into four teams, and give each team a set of coloured blank cards. Teams take turns to select a number card at random, e.g. 3, and cover a number on the grid that has a matching number of tenths, i.e. 0·3, 1·3, 2·3 or 3·3. The winner is the first team to complete a line of four cards in any direction.

Grid addition

Adding 0·1 to a decimal number

Draw a 5 × 2 grid on the board, with a one-place decimal number in each space.

Children copy the grid, writing 0·1 more than each number. When the grid is complete, point to each space in turn, asking a different child to say their answer.

2·4	0·1	0·9	3·7	9·8
19·9	3·25	4·5	2·89	7·91

Number of the week

120

Sample tasks
- Add this number to 230, 340, 425, ...
- Subtract this number from 320, 440, 565, ...
- Count in 20s forwards to/from this number

Sample facts
- It is a multiple of 20.
- It is double 60 and half of 240.
- It is the number of minutes in 2 hours/seconds in 2 minutes.

N42 Addition/subtraction

Nearest estimate

Estimating and completing written subtractions

Divide the class into teams of four or five, and give each team a name. Write a 3-digit subtraction on the board, and ask each team for an immediate estimate of the answer. Write the estimates on the board, next to each team's name. Choose a child to complete the subtraction, using a written procedure. Check the answer with the class. Award points: five for the nearest estimate, four for the next closest etc. Play again.

Nearest hundred

Subtracting one 3-digit number from another

Place-value cards (hundreds), cubes

Each pair writes a 3-digit starter number on a piece of paper. You write a 3-digit number on the board. Allow the pairs a few minutes to find the difference between their number and yours. Choose a place-value card at random, e.g. 500 and hold it up. The five pairs with an answer closest to 500 collect a cube. Repeat.

Word of the week

unit (of measurement)

Sample tasks

- Say some **units** for measuring length. **Units** for length are the metre, centimetre, millimetre, mile, ...
- What does the **unit** millilitre measure? A millilitre is a **unit** for measuring capacity.
- Compare the **units** centimetre and square centimetre. A centimetre is a **unit** of length; a square centimetre is a **unit** of area.

Sample facts

- A **unit** of volume is a cubic centimetre.
- **Units** of time include second, minute, hour, day, week, month, year.
- A millimetre is a small **unit** of length, a kilometre is a large **unit** of length.

N43 Addition/subtraction

Table timer

Adding two amounts whose pence make £1 or £0·50

A timer

Draw the addition tables below.
Children copy the tables, writing the answers to the additions in the appropriate boxes. How quickly can they complete the tables?

a

+	£1·28p
£3·72	
£4·22	
£1·72	
£10·72	

b

+	£2·34
£2·66	
£3·16	
£10·66	
£25·16	

c

+	£5·76
£3·24	
£5·74	
£1·74	
£3·24	

Pounds only

Adding and subtracting amounts of money

A dice

Each pair writes an amount between £1 and £10 on a piece of paper.
Choose a child to throw the dice three times (e.g. 3, 2, 5) and write that amount on the board, e.g. £3·25.
Each pair can choose to find the sum of, or the difference between your number and theirs. Their aim is to make a number as close to a whole number of pounds as possible. Choose pairs to say their answer and whether they chose to add or subtract. Award a point to any pair within 20p of a whole number of pounds. Repeat.

Number of the week

99

Sample tasks

- Add this number to 45, 76, 120, ... by adding 100, then subtracting 1.
- Subtract this number from 145, 267, ... by subtracting 100, then adding 1.
- Say a pair of numbers which differ by this number.

Sample facts

- It is 1 less than 100, the last 2-digit number.
- It is a multiple of 9, and of 11.
- It reads the same forwards and backwards (it is palindromic).

Activity Bank

The Activity Bank includes a variety of activities that address key skills. The activities in the bank can be used at any time alongside any topic, and often you will wish to revisit them throughout the year.

The table lists each activity in the bank, along with the key skill addressed, to help your selection.

Activity	Skill
Place-value and properties of number	
Keep on counting	Counting on and back in steps of constant size
Counting on or back	Counting on and back in ones, tens and hundreds
Watching TV	Understanding the idea of simple proportion

Addition and subtraction	
Match me	Addition bonds to 10 and 20
Open the box	Addition bonds to 9
Table timer	Addition bonds to 10 and 20
Match me	Recognising the next ten
Round the class	Adding 11, 12, 13, 21, 32, 43, ...
Grid addition	Adding 19 and 29
Table timer	Adding two numbers whose units make 10
Number match	Adding two numbers whose units make 10
Number cross	Adding multiples of 10
Right and wrong	Adding 1-digit numbers
Open the box	Adding near doubles
Number cross	Adding multiples of 9
Table timer	Addition bonds to 20 and 50
How many?	Adding multiples of 10
Open the box	Addition bonds to 100
Number match	Addition pairs to 100
Open the box	Estimating the result of adding two 3-digit numbers
Number match	Adding multiples of 100
Right and wrong	Subtracting a 1-digit number from a multiple of 10

Right and wrong	Subtracting a 1-digit number from a 2-digit number
Table timer	Subtracting a 1-digit number from a 2-digit number
Bingo	Subtracting by counting back
Open the box	Subtracting 2-digit numbers from a multiple of 10
Four in a row	Subtracting from a multiple of 10
Right and wrong	Subtracting multiples of 100
Bingo	Subtracting 99, 199, 299, ...
Target numbers	Subtracting 3-digit numbers
Age puzzle	Adding near doubles

Multiplication and division	
Grid doubling	Doubling
Open the box	×3 multiplication facts
Bingo	Multiplying by 4
Right and wrong	Multiplying by 4 and 8
Bingo	Multiplying by 9
Number match	Multiplying by 10
Missing numbers	Multiplying by 10
Number match	Dividing with remainders

Mixed operations	
How many?	Addition, subtraction, doubling
How many?	Adding and halving
How many?	Multiplying and doubling
Target numbers	Adding, subtracting, multiplying, doubling
Target numbers	Adding, subtracting, multiplying, doubling
Target numbers	Adding, subtracting, multiplying, doubling
Target numbers	Adding, place-value

Twenty questions	
Activity 1	Rounding, adding, subtracting, doubling, multiplying
Activity 2	Rounding, adding, subtracting, doubling, multiplying
Activity 3	Rounding, adding, subtracting, doubling, halving, multiplying
Activity 4	Adding, subtracting, doubling, halving, multiplying
Activity 5	Adding, subtracting, doubling, multiplying
Activity 6	Adding, subtracting, doubling, multiplying, fractions
Activity 7	Rounding, adding, subtracting, doubling, multiplying

Activity 8	Rounding, adding, subtracting, doubling, halving, multiplying, dividing, fractions, decimals
Activity 9	Rounding, adding, subtracting, doubling, halving, multiplying, dividing, decimals
Activity 10	Ordering, rounding, adding, subtracting, doubling, multiplying, dividing, decimals
Activity 11	Ordering, rounding, estimating, adding, subtracting, multiplying, dividing, decimals
Activity 12	Ordering, rounding, adding, subtracting, doubling, multiplying, dividing, decimals
Activity 13	Ordering, adding, subtracting, doubling
Activity 14	Ordering, place-value, adding, subtracting, doubling, multiplying, decimals

Solving problems in real life and measures	
Shopping calculation	Solving problems involving money
Exact money only!	Solving problems involving money
How much change?	Solving problems involving money
Music madness	Solving problems involving money
Three of each	Solving problems involving money
How late are we?	Solving problems involving time
Video setting	Solving problems involving time
Football fanatic	Solving problems involving time
Holidays	Solving problems involving time
Millennium teaser	Solving problems involving time

❶ Place-value and properties of number

Keep on counting

Counting on and back in steps of constant size

Divide the class into four teams. Give each team a 'step' number, from 19, 15, 11 and 25.

Write a 2-digit starter number on the board, e.g. 33.

The teams count on in their 'step' from the starter number, passing a piece of paper to the next team member, who writes the next number in the count.

After a few minutes, stop and ask the teams to read out their numbers. Award points for accuracy. Repeat with a larger starter number, counting back.

Counting on or back

Counting on and back in ones, tens and hundreds

Each pair writes a 3-digit number on a piece of paper.

Choose whether to count in ones, tens or hundreds and write this on the board. Point your finger, either up or down, to indicate whether the children should count on, or back.

On your cue the children start counting in their pairs and writing the numbers (in each pair one child should be responsible for writing the numbers counting on, and one for writing the numbers counting back).

After a few moments, ask the children to stop. Vary the count and point either up or down. The children continue from their last number.

After a few minutes, stop and write a target number on the board. Award points to the pairs whose last number is closest to the target.

Watching TV

Understanding the idea of simple proportion

Tell the children to write down roughly the number of hours in one day (a weekday) that they watch television. Next they work in pairs to answer the following questions:

How many hours television do you watch in 24 hours?
How many hours television do you watch in 2 days?
How many hours television do you watch in 5 days?
How many hours television do you watch in 100 days?
How many hours television do you watch in 350 days?

Discuss the various results. About how much television do they watch in a year?

❷ Addition and subtraction

Match me

Addition bonds to 10 and 20

Number cards (0 to 10), one set per child

Select a card at random, hold it up and read it aloud.
The children hold up the number that gives the addition bond to 10.
Repeat for addition bonds to 20, with number cards 0 to 20.

Open the box

Addition bonds to 9

Draw a 5 × 2 grid on the board. Cover each space with a number 0 to 9, and underneath write its addition bond to 9.
Choose a child to point to a box and say its addition bond to 9. Check with the class.
The child can 'open the box' to reveal the answer.

Table timer

Addition bonds to 10 and 20

A timer

Draw a table with three columns. In the left-hand column write the numbers 1 to 9 at random. The children copy the table, writing the addition bonds to 10 in the middle column and to 20 in the right-hand column. How quickly can they complete the table?

	makes 10	makes 20
5		
4		
7		
3		
8		
2		
6		
9		
1		

Match me

Recognising the next ten

Number cards, one set (0 to 9) per child and a set (0 to 50) for the teacher

Select a card at random, hold it up and read it aloud.
Children hold up the number that needs to be added to make the next ten.

Round the class

Adding 11, 12, 13, 21, 32, 43, ...

Write '12, 23, 42' on the board, circling each one.
Choose a child, say a number (e.g. 46) and point to a circle on the board.
The child must add the numbers and say the answer.
If correct the first child chooses another, says a number and points to a circle.
Continue around the class.

Grid addition

Adding 19 and 29

Draw a 6×2 grid on the board, with a 2-digit number in each space.

25	18	34	39	52	47
36	17	43	28	71	55

Children copy the grid adding 19 to each number.
When the grid is complete, point to each space in turn, asking a different child to say the answer.
Repeat for adding 29.

Table timer

Adding two numbers whose units make 10

A timer

Draw a table with two columns. In the left-hand column write 2-digit numbers with 2 units. Children copy the table, adding 18 to each number and writing the answer in the right-hand column. How fast can they complete the table?
Repeat for numbers with 3 units, and adding 17.

	+ 18
12	
22	
52	
32	
72	
82	
92	
62	
42	

	+ 17
13	
23	
73	
33	
43	
93	
83	
63	
53	

Number match

Adding two numbers whose units make 10

Number cards (1 to 100), cubes

Each pair writes a 2-digit multiple of 10 on a piece of paper. Choose a child to pick a card at random and say the number, e.g. 66. Write a number on the board that will make a multiple of 10 when added to the card number, e.g. 24. Each pair adds the two numbers and writes down the answer. If the answer to the addition matches the number they originally wrote on their paper then they can claim a cube. Repeat, choosing a different child to take another card. Continue until one pair has collected three cubes.

Number cross

Adding multiples of 10

Draw a cross on the board with five squares in each 'arm'. Write the numbers '20, 30, 40, 50, 60' next to the cross. Children copy the grid and place the numbers 20 to 60 in the spaces on the vertical arm.
They write numbers in the horizontal arm so that the total across is half the total down. Allow ten minutes, then discuss the different answers.

Right and wrong

Adding 1-digit numbers

Write six additions of several 1-digit numbers on the board, one of which is incorrect. Allow the children five minutes to decide which addition is incorrect.

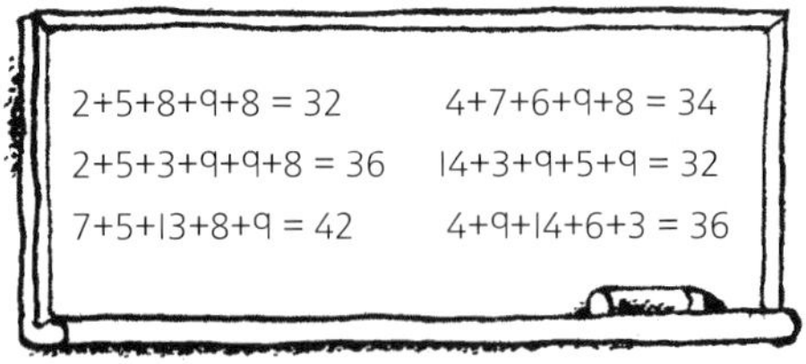

2+5+8+9+8 = 32
4+7+6+9+8 = 34
2+5+3+9+9+8 = 36
14+3+9+5+9 = 32
7+5+13+8+9 = 42
4+9+14+6+3 = 36

Open the box

Adding near doubles

Draw a 5 × 2 grid on the board. Cover each space with an addition of two numbers that are near doubles, and underneath write the answers. Choose a child to point to a box and say the answer. Check with the class. The child can 'open the box' to reveal the answer.

12 + 12	15 + 15	25 + 26	16 + 17	45 + 46
12 + 13	15 + 16	33 + 34	35 + 36	30 + 29

Number cross

Adding multiples of 9

Draw a cross on the board with five squares in each 'arm'. Write '0' in the central square.

Children copy the grid and place the multiples of 9 (9, 18, 27, ... 99) in the spaces so that the total down and across is 198. Allow ten minutes, then discuss the different answers.

Hint: Look for pairs of numbers that total 99.

Table timer

Addition bonds to 20 and 50

A timer

Draw a table with three columns. In the left-hand column write 1- or 2-digit numbers (less than 20) at random.

Children copy the table, writing the addition bond to 20 in the middle column, and the addition bond to 50 in the right-hand column. Who can complete the table fastest?

How many?

Adding multiples of 10

Write '1000' on the board, in a circle. Children work to find ways of adding five multiples of 10 to make the target number, e.g. 200 + 180 + 220 + 140 + 260. Allow ten minutes. Discuss the different answers. Repeat for making 340 from four consecutive multiples of 10 (70 + 80 + 90 + 100).

Open the box

Addition bonds to 100

Draw a 5 × 2 grid on the board. Cover each space with a 2-digit number, and underneath write its bond to 100.

Choose a child to point to a box and say the addition bond to 100. Check with the class. The child can 'open the box' to reveal the answer.

Number match

Addition pairs to 100

Number cards (1 to 9)

Each pair writes a 2-digit number between 25 and 90 and their initials on a piece of paper and passes it along to the next pair. Choose a child to pick two cards at random and use them to make a 2-digit number, e.g. 35. Write this number on the board. Each pair works out what must be added to this number to make 100, i.e. 65. Replace the cards and repeat, choosing a different child to pick another two cards. Continue until the answer matches the number written on one pair's piece of paper.

Open the box

Estimating the result of adding two 3-digit numbers

Draw a 5 × 2 grid on the board. Cover each space with the addition of two 3-digit numbers. Underneath write the approximate answer found by rounding to the nearest ten or hundred. Choose a child to point to a box and estimate the total. Check with the class. The child can 'open the box' to reveal the estimate. How close are the two estimates?

Number match

Adding multiples of 100

Number cards (1 to 9)

Each pair writes a multiple of 100 between 1000 and 2000 on a piece of paper. Choose a child to pick a number card at random and say it aloud, e.g. 6. Write this number of hundreds on the board, i.e.'600'. Replace the card at the bottom of the pile and select a different child to pick another card. Continue until one pair can add some of the multiples to make the number they wrote down originally. Repeat with the children writing new multiples of 10.

Right and wrong

Subtracting a 1-digit number from a multiple of 10

Write ten subtractions of a 1-digit number from a multiple of 10 on the board, one of which is incorrect.
Allow children five minutes to decide which addition is incorrect.

60 – 7 = 53	30 – 4 = 26
50 – 5 = 45	80 – 7 = 73
60 – 9 = 51	40 – 6 = 36
70 – 6 = 64	

Right and wrong

Subtracting a 1-digit number from a 2-digit number

Write six subtractions of 1-digit numbers from 2-digit numbers on the board, one of which is incorrect.
Allow children to decide which subtraction is incorrect.

45 – 8 = 37	36 – 16 = 20
63 – 6 = 57	42 – 7 = 35
22 – 8 = 16	73 – 15 = 58

Table timer

Subtracting a 1-digit number from a 2-digit number

Draw a table with three columns. In the left-hand column write ten
2-digit numbers at random.
The children copy the table, subtracting 6 and writing the answer in the middle column, then subtracting 8 and writing the answer in the right-hand column.
How fast can they complete the table?

	–6	–8
52		
45		
36		
43		
71		
24		
55		
62		
33		

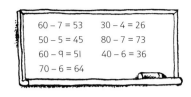

Bingo

Subtracting by counting back

Number cards (1 to 9)

Each pair writes five 2-digit bingo numbers.
Select a card at random, hold it up and read it aloud.
If, by subtracting the card number from one of their bingo numbers the children make an answer with 9 units, they can cross that bingo number out, e.g. 35 – 6 = 29.

Open the box

Subtracting 2-digit numbers from multiples of 10

Draw a 5 × 2 grid on the board. Cover each space with a subtraction of a 2-digit number from its next ten. Underneath write the answer.
Choose a child to point to a box and say the answer.
Check with the class.
The child can 'open the box' to reveal the answer.

Four in a row

Subtracting from a multiple of 10

Number grid (1 to 100), blank cards in three colours

Divide the class into three teams, and give each team a set of coloured blank cards.
Point to a multiple of 10 on the grid, e.g. 60, and a 2-digit number, e.g. 46. Choose a child to subtract the 2-digit number from the multiple of 10 and say the answer. If the child answers correctly the team can cover the answer on the grid with a card of their colour. Continue, choosing a child from each team in turn. The winner is the first team to complete a line of four cards in any direction.

Right and wrong

Subtracting multiples of 100

Write eight subtractions of multiples of 100 from a 3-digit number on the board, some of which are incorrect. Allow the children five minutes to decide which subtractions are incorrect.

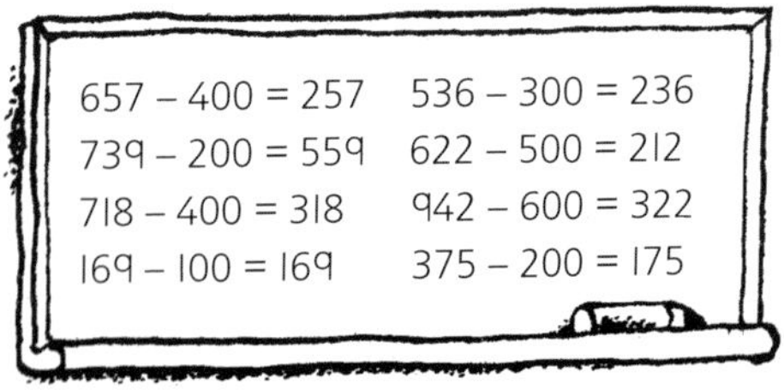

Bingo

Subtracting 99, 199, 299, ...

Number cards (0 to 9)

Each pair writes ten 3-digit bingo numbers.
Select three cards at random to make a 3-digit number.
On the board, write the subtraction of 99, 199, 299, ... (you decide) from the card number.
Choose a child to say the answer.
Any pair with a matching number can cross it out. The first pair to cross out two numbers wins.

Target numbers

Subtracting 3-digit numbers

Write '345, 548, 431, 673, 555' on the board, each in a triangle.
Write '250, 650, 370, 340, 160' on the board, each in a circle.
The children subtract a 3-digit number from a triangle numbers to leave a multiple of 10, e.g. 548 − 138 = 410. Can they make the circle numbers?
Allow ten minutes.
Discuss the answers.

Age puzzle

Adding near doubles

Tell the children this story:
Jack and Jill are brother and sister. Jack is one year older than Jill. Last year their combined ages were a prime number. This year their combined ages are a prime number. Next year their combined ages add up to a number whose digits total 12. How old are they?
Remind the children that they will need to add pairs of near doubles, e.g. 27 + 28.
Allow the pairs five or ten minutes to find the answer (Jack is 37, Jill is 36).

3 Multiplication and division

Grid doubling

Doubling

Draw a 5 × 2 grid on the board, with a 2-digit number in each space.
The children copy the grid, writing double each number.
When the grid is complete, point to each space in turn, asking a different child to say the answer.

32	15	24	25	81
83	53	61	92	67

Open the box

×3 multiplication facts

Draw a 5 × 2 grid on the board. Cover each space with a 1-digit number, and underneath write the matching multiple of 3.
Choose a child to point to a box and multiply by 3. Check with the class.
The child can 'open the box' to reveal the answer.

Bingo

Multiplying by 4

Number cards (1 to 12)

Each pair writes five bingo numbers that are multiples of 4 (up to 48).
Select a card at random, hold it up and read it aloud.
Choose a child to multiply by 4 and say the answer.
Any pair with the matching number can cross it out.

Right and wrong

Multiplying by 4 and 8

Write ten multiplications on the board, some of which are incorrect. Allow children five minutes to decide which multiplications are incorrect.

7 × 4 = 28	8 × 5 = 40
5 × 4 = 20	8 × 4 = 24
6 × 8 = 48	9 × 4 = 38
9 × 8 = 36	3 × 8 = 24
6 × 4 = 24	7 × 8 = 56

Bingo

Multiplying by 9

Number cards (1 to 11)

Each pair writes five bingo numbers that are multiples of 9 (up to 99). Select a card at random, hold it up and read it aloud. Choose a child to multiply by 9.

Any pair with the matching number can cross it out.

Number match

Multiplying by 10

Number cards (2 to 30), cubes

Each pair writes a multiple of 10 between 30 and 300 on a piece of paper. Choose a child to pick a card at random and say the number, e.g. 26. Write this number on the board. Each pair multiplies that number by 10 and writes down the answer. If this number matches the multiple of 10 they originally wrote on their paper, a pair can collect a cube. Repeat, choosing a different child to take another card. Continue until one pair has collected two cubes.

Missing numbers

Multiplying by 10

Write eight multiplications by 10 on the board, each with a missing number.

Point to a missing number and choose a child to tell you what it is. Repeat for each multiplication.

5 × 10 = ●	7 × ● = 70
13 × 10 = ●	● × 10 = 90
● × 10 = 150	23 × 10 = ●
● × 10 = 240	31 × 10 = ●

Number match

Dividing with remainders

Number cards (1 to 9), cubes

Each pair writes a 1-digit number between 1 and 8 on a piece of paper. Write a 2-digit number on the board, e.g. 47. Choose a child to pick a card at random and read it aloud. The children divide the number on the board by the card number and write down the remainder. Any pair who originally wrote down a number that matches the remainder can collect a cube. Replace the card and repeat, writing a new 2-digit number on the board and choosing a different child to take another card. Who collects the most cubes? *What remainder numbers come up most often? Are some numbers better numbers than others to write on your piece of paper?*

4 Mixed operations

How many?

Addition, subtraction, doubling

Write a number on the board, e.g. 24.

The pairs work to find different ways of doubling a number and adding or subtracting another to make the target, e.g. double 7 add 10.

Go round the class asking different pairs for an answer.

How many?

Adding and halving

Write a number on the board, e.g. 9.

The pairs work to find different ways of adding three 1-digit numbers and halving to make the target, e.g. half of $6 + 7 + 5$.

Go round the class asking different pairs for their answers.

How many?

Multiplying and doubling

Write a number on the board, e.g. 192.

The pairs work to find a way of multiplying a number by 8 and doubling to make the target, i.e. doubling 12×8.

Hint: write out the $\times 8$ table first.

Is there more than one solution? Repeat for making 128.

Target numbers

Adding, subtracting, multiplying, doubling

Write '10, 2, 3, 15, 8' on the board, each in a triangle.

Write '108, 360, 150, 400' on the board, each in a circle.

The children choose different triangle numbers, and use adding, subtracting, multiplying or doubling.

Can they make any of the circle numbers?

Allow ten minutes.

Discuss the different answers.

Target numbers

Adding, subtracting, multiplying, doubling

Write '20, 3, 9, 12, 50' on the board, each in a triangle.
Write '1, 200, 5, 7' on the board, each in a circle.
The children choose different triangle numbers, and use adding, subtracting, multiplying or doubling.
Can they make any of the circle numbers?
Allow ten minutes.
Discuss the different answers.

Target numbers

Adding, subtracting, multiplying, doubling

Write '23, 15, 38, 66' on the board, each in a triangle.
Write '142, 178, 54' on the board, each in a circle.
The children choose different triangle numbers, adding, subtracting, multiplying or doubling. As well as each triangle number, children can use its next ten (i.e. 30, 20, 40, 70).
Can they make any of the circle numbers?
Allow ten minutes.
Discuss the different answers.

Target numbers

Adding, place-value

Write '5, 2, 7, 9' on the board, each in a triangle.
Write '12 331, 12 214, 11 584' on the board, each in a circle.
The children arrange the triangle numbers to make different 4-digit numbers.
Can they make any of the circle numbers by adding two of their 4-digit numbers?
Allow ten minutes.
Discuss the different answers.

5 Twenty questions

The following activities cover a range of mathematical topics. They can be used at regular intervals during the course of the year, and you may wish to keep track of the children's scores.
Read out each numbered question, writing them on the board as you read them. Allow about 30 seconds for children to write the answer to each, before moving on to the next question.

Activity 1

18/1/06

1. 14 − 5 = (9)
2. 43 − 5 = (38)
3. Write in figures, four hundred and four. (404)
4. How many threes in 36? (12)
5. Double 14 (28)
6. Double 35 (70)
7. 65 + 30 = (95)
8. 76 + 29 = (105)
9. 137 + 39 = (176)
10. 3 × 10 (30)
11. 13 × 10 (130)
12. 4 + _ = 10 (6)
13. 13 + _ = 20 (7)
14. 35 + _ = 100 (65)
15. Round 37 to its nearest ten. (40)
16. Add 28 to 45. (73)
17. What is 5 less than 84? (79)
18. What is 1 less than 1000? (999)
19. 9 × 9 = (81)
20. What is half of 102? (51)

Activity 2

1. Write three hundred and forty seven in figures. (347)
2. Write six hundred and two in figures. (602)
3. 6 × 5 = (30)
4. 6 × 6 = (36)
5. 6 × 12 = (72)
6. How many fours in 35? (8 r 3)
7. How many fours in 70? (17 r 2)
8. Double 23 (46)
9. Double 28 (56)
10. 42 + 40 (82)
11. 142 + 40 = (182)
12. 54 − 39 = (15)
13. 26 − 9 = (17)
14. 142 − 99 = (43)
15. 43 − 4 = (39)
16. 52 − 4 = (48)
17. What is half of 12? (6)
18. What is half of 102? (51)
19. 1000 − 2 = (998)
20. Round 48 to the nearest ten. (50)

Activity 3

1. Write six hundred and six in figures. (606)
2. Round 124 to the nearest ten. (120)
3. 43 + 44 = (87)
4. 85 + 86 = (171)
5. What's three less than 1000? (997)
6. How many tens in 500? (50)
7. How many fives in 500? (100)
8. 4 × 7 = (28)
9. 67 + 19 = (86)
10. 128 + 99 = (227)
11. 36 − 6 = (30)
12. 64 − 5 = (59)
13. 127 − 18 = (109)
14. 46 + 24 = (70)
15. Double 16 (32)
16. Double 160 (320)
17. What is half of 70? (35)
18. What is half of 74? (37)
19. 15 × 10 = (150)
20. Round 349 to the nearest hundred. (300)

Activity 4

1. Write nine hundred and one in figures. (901)
2. Double 40 (80)
3. Double 55 (110)
4. Double 125 (250)
5. What is the value of 3 in 939? (30)
6. Half of 44 is? (22)
7. Half of 34 is? (17)
8. How many fours in 32? (8)
9. How many fours in 400 (100)
10. 8 × 3 = (24)
11. 36 + 4 = (40)
12. 43 + 8 = (51)
13. 57 + 8 = (65)
14. 54 − 48 = (6)
15. 77 − 7 = (70)
16. 246 + 4 = (250)
17. 362 + 8 = (370)
18. 4 + 9 + 6 + 8 = (27)
19. 14 + 86 = (100)
20. 130 + 100 = (230)

Activity 5

1. 6 × 9 = (54)
2. 7 × 9 = (63)
3. 4 × 9 = (36)
4. Write six hundred and ten in figures. (610)
5. How many nines in 108? (12)
6. How many fours in 36? (9)
7. Double 16 (32)
8. Double 45 (90)
9. 45 + 39 = (84)
10. 24 + 9 = (33)
11. 99 + 99 = (198)
12. 36 − 6 = (30)
13. 46 − 7 = (39)
14. 53 − 8 = (45)
15. 15 + 16 = (31)
16. 45 + 46 = (91)
17. How many sixes in 36? (6)
18. 137 − 8 = (129)
19. 1000 − 1 = (199)
20. 3 × 99 = (297)

Activity 6

1. 18 + 19 = (37)
2. 3 × 4 = (12)
3. 3 × 8 = (24)
4. 3 × 16 = (48)
5. Write four thousand, six hundred and fifty-five in figures. (4655)
6. 25 − 6 = (19)
7. 125 − 7 = (118)
8. Double 36 (72)
9. 47 − 37 = (10)
10. 124 − 24 = (100)
11. 243 − 143 = (100)
12. 123 + 99 = (222)
13. $100 - \frac{1}{2} =$ ($99\frac{1}{2}$)
14. How many half cakes in three whole cakes? (6)
15. 6 × 10 = (60)
16. 16 × 10 = (160)
17. How many nines in 36? (4)
18. How many minutes in three quarters of an hour? (45)
19. 4 + 9 + 8 + 6 + 7 = (34)
20. Double 101 (202)

Activity 7

1. Write one thousand and one in figures. (1001)
2. Round fifty-seven to the nearest ten. (60)
3. Round one hundred and twenty-two to the nearest hundred. (100)
4. Double 17 (34)
5. Double 27 (54)
6. Double 127 (254)
7. 300 − 50 = (250)
8. 910 − 20 = (890)
9. 34 − 7 = (27)
10. 154 − 53 = (101)
11. 267 − 166 = (101)
12. 43 + 29 = (72)
13. 60 − 7 = (53)
14. 130 − 8 = (122)
15. 320 + 99 = (419)
16. 5 × 4 = (20)
17. 15 × 4 = (60)
18. What time is ten minutes later than 8:30? (8:40)
19. 25 + 26 = (51)
20. 46 + 47 = (93)

Activity 8

1. Write one thousand, two hundred and one in figures. (1201)
2. Round one hundred and fifty-one to the nearest hundred. (200)
3. Double 45 (90)
4. Double 46 (92)
5. Halve 28 (14)
6. Halve 120 (60)
7. How many tenths in 0·8? (8)
8. 91 − 6 = (85)
9. 134 − 5 = (129)
10. 3 × 6 = (18)
11. 6 × 6 = (36)
12. 12 × 6 = (72)
13. 24 × 6 = (144)
14. 34 − 15 = (19)
15. 146 − 47 = (99)
16. 16 ÷ 4 = (4)
17. 160 ÷ 4 = (40)
18. What time is ten minutes later than 3:55? (4:05)
19. 25 + 26 = (51)
20. 125 + 126 = (251)

Activity 9

1. Write ten thousand in figures. (10 000)
2. Round one thousand, three hundred and forty-nine to the nearest hundred. (1300)
3. 132 + 8 = (140)
4. 1000 + 10 = (1010)
5. 45 + 6 + 9 = (60)
6. 24 + 25 + 26 = (75)
7. 18 × 10 = (180)
8. 38 × 10 = (380)
9. 99 × 10 = (990)
10. 450 ÷ 10 = (45)
11. 100 × 10 = (1000)
12. Double 56 (112)
13. 4 × 8 = (32)
14. 4 × 6 = (24)
15. 75 − 8 = (67)
16. 175 − 8 = (167)
17. Halve 36 (18)
18. Halve 108 (54)
19. 55 + 56 (111)
20. Write four tenths as a decimal. (0·4)

Activity 10

1. Write ten thousand and one in figures. (10 001)
2. Round nine thousand, nine hundred and forty-nine to the nearest hundred. (9900)
3. 87 + 13 = (100)
4. 46 + 24 = (70)
5. 58 + 33 = (91)
6. 100 − 25 = (75)
7. 100 − 55 = (45)
8. 1000 − 150 = (850)
9. 14 × 10 = (140)
10. 327 × 10 = (3270)
11. Double 32 (64)
12. Double 65 (130)
13. 6 × 6 = (36)
14. 5 × 8 = (40)
15. 5 × 16 = (80)
16. 54 − 7 = (47)
17. 63 − 5 = (58)
18. 99 − 55 = (44)
19. How many fives in 100? (20)
20. Put in order: 2·3 3·2 0·9 1·8 (0·9, 1·8, 2·3, 3·2)

Activity 11

1. Write the number which is five thousand less five. (4995)
2. Round six hundred and forty-nine to the nearest hundred. (600)
3. Estimate the total of 258 + 659. (920/1000)
4. 300 + 400 + 900 = (1600)
5. 465 + 300 = (765)
6. 371 + 199 = (570)
7. 100 − 25 = (75)
8. 100 − 26 = (74)
9. Write in order of size: 2·4, 4·2, 0·4, 0·2 (0·2, 0·4, 2·4, 4·2)
10. 45 − 6 = (39)
11. 32 + 33 = (65)
12. 65 + 66 = (131)
13. 2 × 8 = (16)
14. 4 × 8 = (32)
15. 8 × 8 = (64)
16. 63 − 57 = (6)
17. 200 − 101 = (99)
18. 99 + 98 = (197)
19. How many twos in 100? (50)
20. Put in order: 1042, 1024, 1240, 4020 (1024, 1042, 1240, 4020)

Activity 12

1. Write the number which is two less than two thousand. (1998)
2. Round one thousand, one hundred and eighty-nine to the nearest hundred. (1200)
3. Double 25 (50)
4. Double 75 (150)
5. 65 − 3 = (62)
6. 74 − 5 = (69)
7. 84 − 21 = (63)
8. 57 − 40 = (17)
9. 46 − 25 = (21)
10. 45 − 38 = (7)
11. 32 − 19 = (13)
12. 113 + 34 = (147)
13. 63 + 27 = (90)
14. 46 + 34 = (80)
15. 13 × 10 = (130)
16. 63 × 10 = (630)
17. 6 + 19 = (25)
18. 99 + 99 + 99 = (297)
19. 199 − 100 = (99)
20. Put in order: 8·9, 9·8, 0·9, 0·8 (0·8, 0·9, 8·9, 9·8)

Activity 13

1. Write the number which is 3 more than 998. (1001)
2. 156 + 30 = (186)
3. 163 + 33 = (199)
4. Double 45 (90)
5. Double 95 (190)
6. 14 + _ = 20 (6)
7. 27 + _ = 30 (3)
8. 62 + _ = 70 (8)
9. 43 + _ = 51 (8)
10. 58 + _ = 70 (12)
11. 72 − 39 = (33)
12. 146 + 49 = (195)
13. 400 + 300 = (700)
14. 600 + 700 + 200 = (1500)
15. 65 − 5 = (60)
16. 65 − 8 = (57)
17. 176 − 7 = (169)
18. 1000 − 99 = (901)
19. 147 − 47 = (100)
20. Put in order: 1630, 1163, 1603, 1006, 6000 (1006, 1163, 1603, 1630, 6000)

Activity 14

1. Write the number which is two more than 10 099. (10 101)
2. Which digit indicates the number of thousands in 24 896? (4)
3. 30 + _ = 100 (70)
4. 45 + _ = 100 (55)
5. 62 + _ = 100 (38)
6. 250 + _ = 1000 (750)
7. 4 × 7 = (28)
8. 8 × 7 = (56)
9. 12 × 7 = (84)
10. Double 15 (30)
11. Double 150 (300)
12. 146 + 99 = (155)
13. 73 − 23 = (50)
14. 73 − 24 = (49)
15. 65 − 45 = (20)
16. 65 − 47 = (18)
17. 176 − 49 = (127)
18. 1000 − 99 = (901)
19. 165 − 65 = (100)
20. Put in order: 3·4, 9·9, 1·7, 8·4, 0·9 (0·9, 1·7, 3·4, 8·4, 9·9)

6 Solving problems in real life and measures

Shopping calculation

Solving problems involving money

Divide the class into pairs. Address the class: *Suppose you have £5 to spend between you. You want to buy a magazine each, a chocolate bar costing 25p each, a large bottle of fizzy drink costing 99p, and have enough for your bus fare home, which is 55p each. How much can you afford to spend on each magazine?*

Allow the pairs a few minutes to discuss and agree an answer. Discuss the problem as a class.

Exact money only!

Solving problems involving money

Draw five key rings on the board. Label them with these prices: 62p, £1·05, 50p, 31p, 57p.

Tell the class that each one can be bought using exactly three coins. *Which three coins are needed in each case?*

Allow the pairs a few minutes, then discuss the answers as a class.

Extension: *How much change would you get from a £5 note if you bought all five key rings?*

How much change?

Solving problems involving money

Address the class: *Sanjay and Leila both pay for their magazines with the exact money. The magazines are the same price. Sanjay pays with three silver coins, and Leila pays with five silver coins. How much are the magazines?*

Allow the pairs a few minutes to work on the problem. Discuss how to find the answers with a class.

Music madness

Solving problems involving money

Address the class: *CDs costs £7·99. How many CDs can you afford to buy as presents if you have saved £40? Can you buy a 30p chocolate bar with the change you have left?*

Allow the children a few minutes to find the answer. Discuss the methods they used to work it out. Repeat using different amounts of money.

Three of each

Solving problems involving money

Address the class: *Tomoko has saved three of each type of coin, including three £2 coins. How much has she got? Sam has saved five of every silver coin. Has he got more than Tomoko? What is the difference in their savings?*

Allow the pairs a few minutes to think about the problem. Discuss how to work out the answer.

How late are we?

Solving problems involving time

On the board draw a table and write the times that five children were due at, and the times they actually arrived. In pairs the children work out how late each child was. Allow the pairs a few minutes to agree on the answers. Discuss with the class.

	Due at:	Arrived at:
Emi	quarter past four	ten to five
Stephen	five to ten	quarter past eleven
Dave	half past six	twenty-five to eight
Amar	quarter to eight	twenty to nine
Ruth	five past three	five to five

Video setting

Solving problems involving time

On the board draw a table and write the start times and durations of five different TV programmes. Address the class: *I need to set the video. I know how long each programme lasts, and what time it starts. I need to know the finish time.*

Allow the pairs a few minutes to work out the time that each programme finishes. Discuss with the class. Repeat for some different times.

TV programme	Starts	Lasts
Friends	8:35	45 minutes
EastEnders	8:25	1 hour 5 minutes
The X-Files	9:05	1 hour 10 minutes
The Simpsons	2:15	50 minutes
The Waltons	4:50	55 minutes

Football fanatic

Solving problems involving time

Address the class: *Gianni is a football fanatic. He plays football from when he gets home at 3:45 until tea-time at six o'clock every weekday. On Saturdays and Sundays, he plays all morning from nine to twelve, and then for two hours in the afternoon! How many hours and minutes does Gianni spend playing football each week?*

Allow the children a few minutes to agree an answer, then discuss as a whole class.

Holidays

Solving problems involving time

Explain to the children that a family is trying to plan their holidays. Dad and Mum both get thirty days holiday a year from work. How can they arrange their holidays to have:

- at least two weeks in summer with their children
- at least one week over Christmas and New Year
- a few days at Easter
- a week at the May half-term?

The children plan the holidays for the family, taking into account the school term dates for the current year. Allow the pairs some time to work on the problem, then discuss their different answers.

Millennium teaser

Solving problems involving time

Challenge the children to calculate the number of days in a millennium. Then they should work out how many days there are until the next millennium starts.